JESUS, THE TENDER KING AND HIS REVOLUTIONARY MESSAGE

The Word IN LIFE™ BIBLE DISCOVERY Series

Exploring the Gospel of MATTHEW

THOMAS NELSON PUBLISHERS
Nashville • Atlanta • London • Vancouver

JESUS, THE TENDER KING AND HIS REVOLUTIONARY MESSAGE
The Word In Life™ Bible Discovery Series
Exploring the Gospel of Matthew

Published in Nashville, Tennessee, by Thomas Nelson, Inc.

Written by Joseph Snider.

Printed in the United States of America
1 2 3 4 5 6 7 8 — 00 99 98 97 96

Contents

INTRODUCTION
The Word In Life: God's Word, Your Life

Someone has well said that Scripture was not written merely to be studied, but to change our lives. James exhorts us to be "doers of the word, and not hearers only" (James 1:22), and Jesus said, "By this My Father is glorified, that you bear much fruit; so you will be My disciples" (John 15:8). Clearly, the point of God's Word is not to make us "smarter sinners" but to help us become more like Jesus Christ by making the Word of God part of our lives.

However, applying biblical truth in this day and age is far from easy. In the first place, the fact that the Bible was written thousands of years ago in a different culture can sometimes make it difficult to understand. And even if we grasp what the writers were saying to their original readers, we still must make the connection to our own situation today. In the end, many people wonder: Can Scripture really make any difference in our complex, modern world? Yes it can, and this publication helps to show the way.[1]

If the soil of your heart is prepared for planting, studying God's Word is like seeding a whole garden. The seed is good, so expect a bountiful harvest!

But if the soil of your heart is resistant, the Word can be like a hammer breaking down barriers to the truth. Don't be surprised if God's Word knocks you about some.

Fire is another metaphor for God's Word. It purifies, exposing and removing dross in order to reveal the value of what was there all along.

The Word of God also will put a song on your lips—songs of praise to God for His goodness, or songs of contentment that all is well between you and God.

The Word In Life™ Bible Discovery Guide *is designed to help you plant the seeds, to give you wisdom for understanding the constructive hammer blows and purifying flames, to show you the score for the song—to help you hear and understand God's Word in your life. This Guide will help you to*

- *Observe life in the Word—in the stories and sayings, people, places, and events of the Bible.*
- *Explore their meaning for then and now, for there and here.*
- *Personalize their meaning for you, today; and*
- *Experience the Word in your life!*

Keyed to the innovative, user-friendly Word In Life™ Study Bible, *this Guide will help you use its features to the max (although you can also use it with any Bible). And the Guide is designed for individual use and for use by small groups (with a section for leaders).*

Like the Word In Life™ Study Bible *itself, this* Bible Discovery Guide *is concerned with understanding and applying the Bible to daily life. Look for emphasis upon applying God's Word to your work and your public life as well as to your character and your personal relationship with Jesus Christ.*

Enjoy the Word of God. Let it get into your life and make it deep and rich in the wisdom and character of God as revealed in His Son and applied by His Holy Spirit.

1. *The Word In Life™ Study Bible: New Testament Edition* (Nashville, TN: Thomas Nelson Publishers, 1993), vii.

LESSON 1

No Ordinary Beginning, No Ordinary King

Matthew 1:1—2:23

Who can forget the breathtaking footage of the Austrian Alps in the opening to The Sound of Music. *Right away you know that grandeur and majesty will play a role in what follows. A single French horn or violin whispers phrases and themes from the musical as you watch the terrible beauty of a craggy mountain pinnacle or the loveliness of an Alpine lake. There is a hush in the presence of God's handiwork.*

With increasing speed the camera closes on a mountain meadow where a solitary female figure spreads her arms to embrace the beauty of spring. The shift from panorama to close-up lets you know that the mountains and the maiden are connected. In some way she shares their majesty. But you don't know how. It will be some time into the story before you understand that Maria is anything more than a country girl who can't quite find her place in life.

The Gospel of Matthew begins with a grand sweep through the personalities of the Old Testament from Abraham to David, through the kings of Judah and their descendants to a man named Joseph, whose wife gave birth to a special son. Angels and dreams attend that birth. Persian astrologers hail Him; the king of Judea plots to kill Him. The family flees to Egypt until the coast is clear and they can return to Nazareth of Galilee.

This can be no ordinary child. There is something awesome about Him. But only the events of the rest of the story can tell us how the majesty of His birth works itself out in the carpenter's son who was, in fact, the tender King with the most revolutionary message the world has heard.

No Ordinary Gospel

A quick glance through the writings of the early church fathers shows that they liked Matthew best of the four Gospels. Matthew recorded more of the teaching of Jesus than the other gospel writers. This was important to the early church because Jesus had commanded His disciples to "make disciples of all nations, . . . teaching them to observe all the things that I have commanded you" (Matt. 28:19, 20). Matthew taught the early church—and ours too—what to teach new disciples.

CONSIDER THIS

Read the *Word in Life™ Study Bible (WILSB)* feature "A Christian Torah" (Introduction to Matthew). "In Jesus' day, the Pentateuch was known as the Torah. . . . Both the hearing and the doing of the Law made the Torah . . . . In the same way, Matthew balances the teaching of Christ with the application of that truth in day-to-day life. He builds his material around five major speeches that Jesus gave, producing a sort of five-volume 'Christian Torah.'"

Quickly read each of the following five major blocks of teaching by Jesus in Matthew. Record a brief summary of His message.

◆ Kingdom Ethics[1] (Matt. 5—7)

. . . .

. . . .

◆ Kingdom Mission (Matt. 10)

. . . .

. . . .

◆ Kingdom Presence (Matt. 13)

. . . .

. . . .

◆ Kingdom Order (Matt. 18)

. . . .

. . . .

◆ The Kingdom's Future (Matt. 24—25)

. . . .

FOR YOUR INFO

Read the *WILSB* features "Matthew, the Social Outcast" and "Personality Profile: Matthew" (Introduction to Matthew). Based on this material and the accounts in Matthew 9:9–13; Mark 2:14–17; and Luke 5:27–32, answer the following questions:

Why was Matthew despised by most of his contemporaries?

. . . .

. . . .

How would Jesus' calling of Matthew as one of the twelve disciples show the revolutionary character of Jesus' kingdom?

. . . .

. . . .

Why do you think Matthew may have had a special interest in the teachings that new disciples needed?

. . . .

. . . .

CONSIDER THIS

Read the *WILSB* feature "A Global Gospel with a Jewish Accent" (Introduction to Matthew). "In Jesus, all of us can find hope, no matter what our ethnic background." We don't have to be Jewish to be eligible for God's blessing and salvation.

Matthew abounds with Old Testament quotations that reveal that Jesus of Nazareth fulfilled the prophecies concerning the Messiah of Israel. For instance, scan Matthew 1:18—2:23. How many Old Testament quotations did you find?

. . . .

. . . .

What was Matthew demonstrating by means of those quotations?

. . . .

. . . .

Matthew is not a gospel limited to interests in the Jewish people and religion. Read the following passages from Matthew 3:9; 8:5–11; 15:21–28; 24:14; 28:19. What message did Jesus proclaim about Gentiles and His kingdom?

. . . .

. . . .

◆ No Ordinary King ◆

(Matthew 1:1–17)

Matthew begins with a genealogy—one of those lists of names that traces someone's ancestry through dozens of generations. Many "practical" Bible readers skip right over these lists. But Matthew had some important things to say about Jesus by means of His ancestry. Take a closer look.

CONSIDER THIS

Read the *WILSB* feature "Jesus' Roots" (Matt. 1:1–16). From this feature and Matthew 1:1–17, answer the following questions.

With which historical figures did Matthew particularly want to connect Jesus? (Matt. 1:1) ____________________ and _______________ Why these two?

....

....

What four people or events divide the genealogy into important epochs? (Matt. 1:17)

◆ (1)..

....

◆ (2)..

....

◆ (3)..

....

◆ (4)..

....

CONSIDER THIS

Read the *WILSB* feature "The Women in Jesus' Genealogy" (Matt. 1:3–6). "Much has been made of the Virgin Mary, but Matthew's genealogy (vv. 1–16) highlights four other women in Jesus' family. They were touched by scandal and remembered as 'sinners' and 'foreigners.'" Jewish genealogies typically ignored women. Readers would expect those included to be exceptionally noble. Matthew must have had a special purpose for featuring "scandalous" women. What scandal was associated with each of these?

◆ Tamar (Matt. 1:3; see Gen. 38)

◆ Rahab (Matt. 1:5; see Josh. 2:1–24)

◆ Ruth (Matt. 1:5; see Ruth; Deut. 23:3–6)

◆ Bathsheba (Matt. 1:6; 2 Sam. 11—12)

What scandal was associated with Mary, the mother of Jesus? (Matt. 1:18, 19)

CONSIDER THIS

Read the *WILSB* feature "What It Means To Be Like Jesus #1" (Matt. 1:1–17). "If we want to be like [Jesus], we need to understand and accept our roots in terms of culture, race, gender, and reputation. Moreover, like Jesus we want to avoid demeaning anyone else's heritage."

What parts of your background or present history are you tempted to conceal as embarrassing?

How does that background or present history influence who you are?

Why is it important for you to be honest and forthright about your roots?

No Ordinary Birth

(Matthew 1:18–25)

If Jesus was only the kind of King who fulfilled the promises made to David and the prophecies made about the return from the captivity, we would expect Him to be born in a palace. But since Jesus was also the kind of King who cared about courageous women who persevered through scandal, we shouldn't be surprised that He identified with outsiders in His birth

First-century Jewish betrothals (a binding form of engagement) could be dissolved only by an actual divorce. The story of this one is told from Joseph's perspective. What was his dilemma (Matt. 1:18, 19)?

. . . .

. . . .

From Matthew 1:20, 21, what do you learn or infer about each of the following?

◆ Mary

. . . .

. . . .

◆ Joseph (see 24, 25 also)

. . . .

. . . .

◆ Jesus

. . . .

. . . .

CONSIDER THIS

Read Matthew 1:22, 23 and the *WILSB* feature "What's in a Name?" (Matt. 1:23). "Jesus does not take us out of the turmoil and pain of daily life, but rather walks *with us* as we live life."

Jesus had one divine "parent" and one human parent. How did the virgin birth help Him bridge the gap between God and humans?

. . . .

. . . .

What does the genealogy and the birth narrative suggest to you about the ways in which God is "with us" in the person of Jesus?

. . . .

. . . .

If God is with you in Jesus during all of the struggles and difficulties of life, how should that affect your attitude and approach toward them?

. . . .

. . . .

No Ordinary Childhood
(Matthew 2:1–23)

Once Jesus identified with outsiders in His birth, He faced one strange occurrence after another as a very young child. Notice how each incident (starting with Matt. 1:18) contains reference to at least one Old Testament passage. When God comes among people, He starts to carry out His plans for the well-being of all who will receive His grace.

Even as an infant Jesus caused divisions among people based on their perceptions of who He was. Matthew 2 opens by introducing "wise men from the East" (v. 1). Wise men were "magi" (from which we get "magician") or astrologers who practiced occult arts forbidden in the Old Testament (Deut. 18:11). Those who should have been blinded by occultism glimpsed the light of "God with us" while those whose spiritual eyes should have been accustomed to the light were blinded by self-interest.

A CLOSER LOOK

Read the *WILSB* features "Herod the Great" (Matt. 2:3) and "The Herods" (Acts 12:1, 2). "Herod the Great (v. 3) was a highly ambitious leader who would stop at nothing to advance or protect his position."

Both the wise men and Herod received the same information about the identity of Jesus as King of the Jews (Matt. 2:2–6). What character qualities did the wise men have that led them to worship Jesus while Herod lacked them and rejected Him?

. . . .

. . . .

Why do you think people in power have difficulty accepting Jesus as the King of their lives?

. . . .

. . . .

What connection do you suppose there was between Herod's inquiry about the time when the wise men first saw the star announcing the birth of the King of the Jews and his decision to kill all male babies two years old and younger? (Matt. 2:7, 16)

. . . .

. . . .

What was ironic about pagan wise men worshiping Jesus while King Herod was plotting to kill Him? (Matt. 2:11, 16)

. . . .

. . . .

CONSIDER THIS

Read the *WILSB* feature "A Poor Family Comes into Wealth" (Matt. 2:11). "The costly gifts probably represented more wealth than either [Joseph or Mary] had seen in a lifetime. . . . In this instance, offerings of worship may have paid for a journey to Egypt and a new life in a strange land."

What is the most lavish and extravagant gift you have ever given the Lord as an act of worship?

. . . .

. . . .

How can you worship the Lord in ways that provide meaningful assistance to needy people—either Christians or non-Christians?

. . . .

. . . .

In the light of their own historical exodus from Egypt, what do you think it meant to early Jewish Christians that Jesus also had fled to Egypt and returned from there? (Matt. 2:13–15)

. . . .

. . . .

CONSIDER THIS

Read the *WILSB* feature "What It Means To Be Like Jesus #2" (Matt. 1:18—2:23). "If we want to be like Jesus, we need to face up to the world and remain very much in it, despite all its troubles."

Which particular "pains of the world" would you like to avoid? Why?

. . . .

. . . .

Why do you think Jesus wants His followers to involve themselves with the "pains of the world"?

. . . .

. . . .

Which "pains of the world" do you sense the Lord wants you to be involved in relieving?

. . . .

. . . .

CONSIDER THIS

Read the *WILSB* feature "City Kids Die over Adult Matters" (Matt. 2:16–18). Rachel (v. 18) had been one of Jacob's wives. She died in childbirth (Gen. 35:16–20). Jeremiah later had imagined Rachel mourning the children who died during the Babylonian invasion of Judah (Jer. 31:15). Matthew extended her grief to cover Herod's murder of the children at Bethlehem.

How do you think Jesus' memory of this incident shaped His attitude toward children?

. . . .

. . . .

How can Christians today offer practical help to urban children around the world who are abused or neglected by powerful people?

. . . .

. . . .

"Nazareth was a despised place (John 7:42, 52) even to other Galileans (cf. John 1:46). Here Jesus grew up, not as 'Jesus the Bethlehemite,' with its Davidic overtones, but as 'Jesus the Nazarene,' with all the opprobrium of a sneer."[2]

Why do you think such an extraordinary King and Savior chose to grow up in obscurity?

. . . .

. . . .

◆ ◆ ◆ ◆ ◆ ◆ ◆ ◆

On the following chart summarize the ways in which Jesus' coming portrayed in Matthew 1:1—2:23 does not match the ways you would expect a powerful leader to come into the world.

WHAT I WOULD NORMALLY EXPECT	HOW JESUS ACTUALLY CAME
Example: worldwide announcement	**Example:** not widely publicized

. . . .

. . . .

. . . .

. . . .

Write a prayer of adoration addressed to Jesus expressing your thoughts about His willingness to become "God with us" in the way He did.

. . . .

. . . .

1. Teaching titles are adapted from Craig S. Keener, *The IVP Bible Background Commentary: New Testament* (Downers Grove, IL: InterVarsity Press, 1993), 45.

2. D.A. Carson, "Matthew," *The Expositor's Bible Commentary,* Vol. 8 (Grand Rapids, MI: Zondervan Publishing House, 1984), 97.

The Tender King's Revolutionary Righteousness

Matthew 3:1—7:20

One of the first themes of the Gospel of Matthew is the revolutionary righteousness Jesus expects of those who would be citizens of His kingdom. "Righteousness" is a difficult word—other-worldly and unattainable. There were all sorts of ordinary religious teachers in Jesus' day with ordinary messages explaining ordinary ideas about righteousness. Jesus said none of them were good enough. He would have no ordinary righteousness. In the Sermon on the Mount Jesus unfolded His manifesto of revolutionary righteousness. Explore these early chapters of Matthew to discover the ethic of the kingdom of heaven. They're a real eye-opener.

No Ordinary Teacher Certification

Matthew 3:1—5:16

On his first day of high school, Bob heard Mrs. Hawthorne coming before he saw her. Her high heels clicked on the tiles in the hallway as though she were running to class. She steamed in with a scowl on her face that indicated extreme concentration and a no-nonsense-from-you attitude. She was small, and her sudden movements made Bob think of a bird darting through the branches of a tree. "This is the end of me," he thought.

Instead it was a beginning. Mrs. Hawthorne was a teacher who loved Latin almost as much as she loved students. Her unconscious scowl gave way readily to peals of laughter that could be heard three rooms away. She slaved over homework papers, scrawling messages by the paragraph. But students looked only for an exultant "Bene" ("well done") bannered across the top.

A student wrote an operetta about Caesar's conquest of Gaul in the style of Gilbert and Sullivan. Never were the Gallic wars funnier. Another parodied the then-popular song "Who Put the Bop in the Bop Sha-Bop Sha-Bop" and called it "Who Put the Tu in the Tu, Tui, Tibi, Te." The song featured verses on various Latin personal, relative, and demonstrative pronouns. Mrs. Hawthorne shrieked with glee, although the class had to sing the original song for her before she got the joke.

Mrs. Hawthorne was no ordinary teacher. Many students wrongly thought she was mean and harsh. She was certified as a great teacher by the witnesses of minds and lives enriched by her influence. Those who loved her visited her repeatedly after graduation to find that she remembered every one of their accomplishments and successes.

In a similar way Jesus proved He was a teacher—a teacher of revolutionary righteousness. He was certified by the voice of God, by victory over the devil, and by a stunning declaration of revolutionary righteousness.

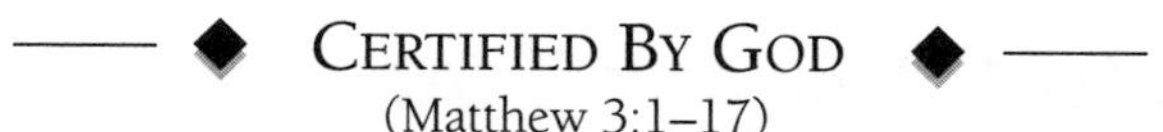

Certified By God
(Matthew 3:1–17)

Before Jesus taught a single word to His first disciple, His credentials were attested by the highest authorities. God Himself declared Jesus to be the spokesman for the kingdom of heaven. First He made advance preparations through His prophet John the Baptist, and then He made a personal declaration about Jesus at the time of His baptism.

CONSIDER THIS

Read the *Word in Life™ Study Bible (WILSB)* feature "John the Street Preacher (Matt. 3:4). "Would John the Baptist (v. 4) have been comfortable using today's media to proclaim his startling message? Probably not." John lived austerely and proclaimed a demanding message that needed to be delivered personally and simply.

How did John's mission and message require him to live and act as he did?

How can mass methods and social acceptability dilute the impact of basic messages about the Lord?

Who has had an impact like that of John in your life— bold, blunt, and honest? How have you benefited?

What kind of person would you choose to head up the campaign of the next president of the United States? Who should introduce the leader of the people to them?

How does your choice compare and contrast with John the Baptist, God's choice to introduce Jesus to His people?

What is significant about the contrasts between your choice and God's?

. . . .

. . . .

CONSIDER THIS

Read the *WILSB* feature "The Power of Humility" (Matt. 3:11). "If you regard strength as the power to dominate, you'll always be intimidated by those who seem to have more than you—more expertise, more experience, more energy, more intelligence. John held a different understanding of strength."

In what area(s) of your life are you most easily intimidated by people who have more of "what it takes" than you?

. . . .

. . . .

In what area(s) of your life are you most competent?

. . . .

. . . .

How can you accept humbly the advantages of those who are more gifted than you?

. . . .

. . . .

John did not want to baptize Jesus because he realized that Jesus was more righteous than he. Jesus insisted that John baptize Him in order to "fulfill all righteousness" (Matt. 3:15). In this way Jesus obeyed His Father, accepted His mission as the Savior who would suffer for sins, and identified Himself with the repentant sinners who looked forward to the kingdom of heaven.

In what ways has God impressed on you that Jesus is His Son and should be listened to?

. . . .

. . . .

CONSIDER THIS

Read the *WILSB* feature "What It Means To Be Like Jesus #3" (Matt. 3:1–17). "If we want to be like Jesus, we must not pick and choose our brothers and sisters in God's family. We need to embrace other believers and demonstrate our unity in Christ, no matter how awkward or inconvenient."

What kinds of Christians do you avoid because they embarrass you?

. . . .

What kinds of Christians do you avoid because they frustrate you or make you mad?

. . . .

What kinds of Christians do you avoid because you disagree with them?

. . . .

How can you express love to different kinds of people in the body of Christ in spite of significant differences in theology, style of worship, and ways of relating to the world around you?

. . . .

What character qualities do you need to be able to accept God's truth from someone with whom you aren't comfortable?

. . . .

◆ Certified By Testing ◆

(Matthew 4:1–11)

In many ways Matthew presents Jesus as the ideal Son of God in comparison to Israel, the failed son of God. Like Israel, Jesus had gone down into Egypt and returned (Matt. 2:14, 15, 19, 21). In Matthew 4, Jesus, like Israel of old, went into the desert—for forty days instead of forty years—and underwent a time of testing. Israel failed all of its tests in the wilderness; Jesus succeeded in all of His.

CONSIDER THIS

Read the *WILSB* feature "You Don't Understand!" (Matt. 4:3). "How often we hear someone dismiss the implications of faith for day-to-day life with the retort, 'You don't understand! I live in the real world, where things are tough.'" The temptation pictures Jesus successfully facing the pressures of the "real world."

Jesus faced every temptation during His entire life without yielding to one of them. Some people wrongly conclude that He never found out how hard it really is to struggle with sin because He never gave in. Why is it harder to resist every temptation than to give in to some of them?

. . . .

. . . .

What do you think Jesus learned about temptation from experiencing it that gives Him insight into the temptations you face every day?

. . . .

. . . .

The first temptation Jesus faced involved His physical needs and desires. On the following scale, circle the number that indicates the strength of the appeal of physical temptations to your personality and spirit.

1 2 3 4 5 6 7 8 9 10

BORING — MILDLY INTERESTING — VERY APPEALING — OVER-WHELMING

The second temptation of Jesus attacked His sense of personal importance or value. On the following scale, circle the number that indicates the strength of the appeal of various forms of pride to your personality and spirit.

1 2 3 4 5 6 7 8 9 10

UNMOVED — SELF-PITY — SELF-PROTECTION — SELF-ASSERTION — SELF-ABSORPTION

Jesus' third wilderness temptation by the devil focused on His desire for power, wealth, and prestige. On the following scale, circle the number that indicates the strength of the appeal of various forms of greed to your personality and spirit.

1 2 3 4 5 6 7 8 9 10

CONTENT — WOULD ENJOY MORE — ACTIVELY SEEK MORE — OBSESSED WITH MORE

CONSIDER THIS

Read the *WILSB* feature "Wealth's Temptation" (Matt. 4:8–10). "For us who live in a materialistic culture, it's good to recognize that the desire for wealth and all that it symbolizes—prestige, power, luxury, authority—can be a powerful tool in Satan's hands."

How do money or things awaken greed or anxiety in you?

. . . .

. . . .

How does the issue of whom you are going to serve (Matt. 4:10) affect your greed or anxiety?

. . . .

. . . .

CONSIDER THIS

Read the *WILSB* feature "What It Means To Be Like Jesus #4" (Matt. 4:1–11). "If we want to be like Jesus, we must accept that temptation is real—as is the possibility of overcoming temptation."

What temptations do you need to be more honest with yourself about (facing your need to deal with them)?

. . . .

. . . .

What temptations do you need to be more honest with God about (facing your moral guilt)?

. . . .

. . . .

What temptations do you need to be more honest with other people about (facing your need to repair damage)?

. . . .

. . . .

◆ ACCLAIMED BY THE PUBLIC ◆

(Matthew 4:12–25)

Jesus continued in Judea from the time of His baptism until John the Baptist was imprisoned (Matt. 4:12). Then He withdrew to His native territory of Galilee in northern Palestine. Instead of remaining in little Nazareth, Jesus transferred His residence to Capernaum, a major fishing center on the northern shores of the Sea of Galilee (v. 13). There Jesus enjoyed immediate popular acclaim when He began His public ministry of teaching.

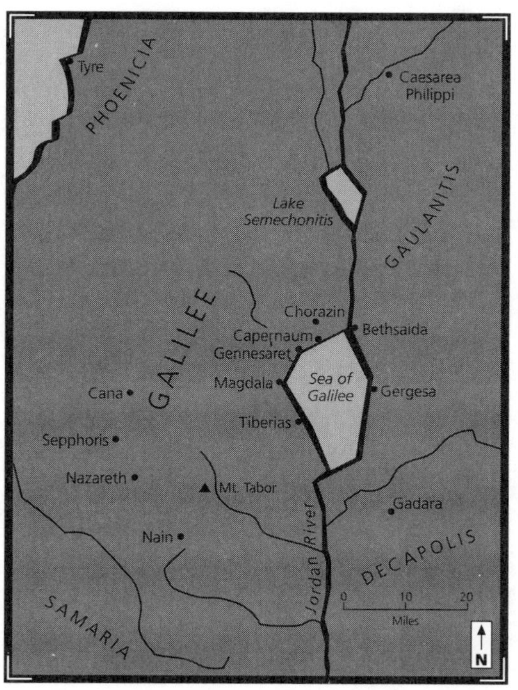

Once in Capernaum, Jesus began preaching the same message John the Baptist had proclaimed in Judea: "Repent, for the kingdom of heaven is at hand" (Matt. 4:17, see 3:2). What had John meant by the message, and what did Jesus mean by it?

. . . .

. . . .

Why is repentance necessary before you can legitimately welcome the Lord as King of your life?

. . . .

. . . .

CONSIDER THIS

Read the *WILSB* feature "The King Declares His Kingdom" (Matt. 4:17). "The kingdom has to do with whatever Christ the King rules." What has changed in each of these areas because Christ now rules your life?

◆ Your allegiance

. . . .

. . . .

◆ Your expectations

. . . .

. . . .

◆ Your values

. . . .

. . . .

◆ Your priorities

. . . .

. . . .

◆ Your lifelong mission

. . . .

. . . .

Before Jesus called the Galilean fishermen to be His permanent disciples, He had met them in Judea when they were following John the Baptist (John 1:35–51). Indeed, they may have listened to Jesus teach just the day before He called them (Luke 5:1–11).

Peter, Andrew, James, and John left secure family businesses in order to announce the kingdom of heaven. What has the Lord replaced in your life with the commission to share the good news?

. . . .

. . . .

From a Jewish viewpoint, Syria (Matt. 4:24) was Gentile Palestine to the north of Galilee. To the Romans, Syria included all of Palestine, Jew and Gentile. Decapolis and the area beyond the Jordan (v. 25) were Gentile territories, so Matthew makes it clear that the message of the kingdom of heaven reached beyond the Jewish people from the earliest phases of Jesus' ministry. How have you seen the gospel escape "polite society" to touch truly needy people?

. . . .

. . . .

CONSIDER THIS

Read the *WILSB* feature "What It Means to Be Like Jesus #5" (Matt. 4:12–25). "We need to verbally declare our faith if we want to be like Christ. . . . What we tell others gives meaning to our quiet walk and good deeds."

What can our lives alone communicate to others about the kingdom of heaven?

. . . .

. . . .

What must our words add to our lives to complete the message about the kingdom of heaven?

. . . .

. . . .

Attested by His Message

(Matthew 5:1–16)

It's one thing to know that Jesus proclaimed the arrival of the kingdom of heaven and that multitudes flocked to hear Him. It's quite another thing to know the content of Jesus' message about the kingdom. Matthew recorded the Sermon on the Mount to tell us what our lives should be like after we repent of our sins and embrace His reign.

CONSIDER THIS

Read the *WILSB* feature "The Way Up Is Down" (Matt. 5:3). "Of all the virtues Christ commended in the Beatitudes, it is significant that the first is humility, being 'poor in spirit' (v. 3). That underlies all the others."

Paraphrase each of the Beatitudes, showing how they relate to humility. (The first two are completed for you as examples.)

◆ Poor in spirit (Matt. 5:3). The truly happy are those who know they are needy, not self-sufficient.

. . . .

. . . .

◆ Those who mourn (Matt. 5:4). The truly happy are moved by suffering around them, not callously indifferent and self-centered.

. . . .

. . . .

◆ The meek (Matt. 5:5).

. . . .

. . . .

◆ Those who hunger and thirst for righteousness (Matt. 5:6).

. . . .

. . . .

◆ The merciful (Matt. 5:7).

. . . .

. . . .

◆ The pure in heart (Matt. 5:8).

. . . .

. . . .

◆ The peacemakers (Matt. 5:9).

. . . .

. . . .

◆ The persecuted (Matt. 5:10).

. . . .

. . . .

When Jesus called on His followers to rejoice in persecution (Matt. 5:1–12), He was not asking us to take masochistic pleasure in pain. How can a spiritually and emotionally healthy disciple draw a positive conclusion from the hostility of evil people?

. . . .

. . . .

What do you think it means to be blessed by God (Matt. 5:3–12)?

. . . .

. . . .

How do the Beatitudes stand in revolutionary contrast with what the world typically understands to be the best things in life?

. . . .

. . . .

CONSIDER THIS

Read the *WILSB* feature "Sulfa Drugs and Street Lights" (Matt. 5:13–16). "Following Christ goes far beyond private spirituality. It also involves a believer's public life, particularly through work and participation in the community. Jesus used two metaphors to describe that dynamic: salt (v. 13) and light (vv. 14–16)."

How do you think Christians can act as salt in the world to preserve culture by slowing or halting decay?

. . . .

. . . .

How do you think Christians can act as light in the world to illuminate the truth and to show people the way into the kingdom of heaven?

. . . .

. . . .

◆ Matthew 5:1–16 does not sound like an ordinary king laying the groundwork for an ordinary kingdom. What are the main ideas from these verses that let you know Jesus was the tender King announcing His revolutionary kingdom?

◆ The King

. . . .

. . . .

◆ His kingdom

. . . .

. . . .

LESSON 3

Getting to the Spirit of the Law

Matthew 5:17—6:18

Antonio, the title character in Shakespeare's The Merchant of Venice, *borrowed 3000 ducats from the moneylender Shylock to finance his friend's courtship of Portia. At the time all of Antonio's capital was tied up in fleets of ships off to distant lands, but they were all expected in port before his note to Shylock was due. Besides, Shylock had played a friendly little game. If Antonio forfeited his debt, he didn't owe a real penalty. The contract called for Shylock to carve a pound of Antonio's flesh from his chest right next to his heart. The two men had laughed over the jest.*

Incredibly, all of Antonio's merchant fleets failed to return and were assumed lost at sea; he was bankrupt. Suddenly, Shylock disclosed his secret loathing of Antonio and his intention to have his pound of flesh. A court date was set to determine if the contract was binding.

Wise and courageous Portia traveled incognito to Venice and impersonated the judge at Antonio's trial. She upheld the legality of Shylock's claim of a pound of flesh but appealed to him to modify with mercy the letter of the law. Shylock refused to be merciful and extolled the strictest interpretation of the law.

Then Portia sprang her trap woven from the letters of various laws. Shylock could have Antonio's flesh but none of his blood. Venetian law forbade the shedding of Christian blood by Jewish hands. Another statute ruled the forfeit of property of any noncitizen who made an attempt on the life of a citizen.

Shylock tried to use the letter of the law to revenge himself on his enemy. Instead the merciless letter of the law destroyed him.

Jesus taught in the Sermon on the Mount the revolutionary idea that the spirit of the law is more important, and often more demanding, than the letter. The tender Messiah agreed with Portia that mercy

is an attribute to God himself;
And earthly power doth then show likest God's
When mercy seasons justice.[1]

The spirit of the law consists of both grace and truth.

Revolt Against Externals 

(Matthew 5:17–32)

Jesus believed that the whole Old Testament prepared the way for Him. All of the spiritual content of the Law and Prophets found their ultimate fulfillment in Him. That gave Jesus the right to point out to His listeners what the Old Testament meant. They had heard all sorts of teaching in their lifetime, but Jesus could straighten out every misinterpretation.

CONSIDER THIS

Read the *Word in Life Study Bible (WILSB)* feature "The Morality of Christ" (Matt. 5:17-48). "The [Jewish] people were taught a heavily doctored version of the Old Testament by their rabbis. Sometimes these teachers stressed the letter of the Law rather than its spirit, and sometimes they favored their own traditions over the actual teaching of God."

What had some listeners assumed was Jesus' attitude toward the Old Testament? (Matt. 5:17)

What was Jesus' attitude toward the Old Testament? (Matt. 5:18, 19)

Jesus insisted that His followers be more righteous than the scribes and Pharisees (Matt. 5:20). What do you think that demand has to do with the way Jesus contrasted the spirit of the Law with common understandings of its letter?

How do you think you can recognize teachers and preachers who confuse human traditions with the spirit of God's Word?

CONSIDER THIS

Read the *WILSB* features "What About the Old Testament Law?" (Matt. 5:19) and "Ten Commandments for Practical Living" (James 2:8–13). "While God does not require us to live by the specific regulations of the Old Testament Law, He still expects us to honor Old Testament morality."

Read the Ten Commandments (Ex. 20:2–17) and the Beatitudes (Matt. 5:3–10). What do you think the two sets of instructions have to do with one another?

. . . .

. . . .

What is the greatest ethical shortcoming you observe during the course of your daily routine? Which commandment and which Beatitude do you think would make the greatest improvement?

. . . .

. . . .

Summarize the popular letter of the law about murder and Jesus' authoritative teaching about its spirit. (Matt. 5:21–26)

◆ The letter of the law

. . . .

. . . .

◆ The spirit of the law

. . . .

. . . .

Who have you provoked to anger by the way you have behaved toward them in each of these settings?

◆ Family

. . . .

. . . .

◆ Work

. . . .

. . . .

◆ Church

. . . .

. . . .

What should you do to resolve these angry relationships?

. . . .

. . . .

Jesus loved to make His point with bold, memorable statements. Some of them are exaggerated for effect, such as His suggestions of self-mutilation in Matthew 5:29. Jesus stated much of the Sermon on the Mount in bold terms that are difficult to fulfill literally. He expected His first-century listeners and His twentieth-century readers to apply the spirit of His words.

Summarize the popular letter of the law about adultery and Jesus' authoritative teaching about its spirit. (Matt. 5:27–30)

◆ The letter of the law

. . . .

. . . .

◆ The spirit of the law

. . . .

. . . .

Contemporary advertising and entertainment celebrate lust as an important human quality. What appeals to lust do you need to resist and what stimuli do you need to avoid?

◆ Resist

. . . .

. . . .

◆ Avoid

. . . .

. . . .

Summarize the popular letter of the law about adultery and Jesus' authoritative teaching about its spirit. (Matt. 5:27–30)

◆ The letter of the law

. . . .

. . . .

◆ The spirit of the law

. . . .

. . . .

◆ Revolt Against Evil ◆

(Matthew 5:33–48)

Jesus pointed out in the Sermon on the Mount that some parts of the Old Testament were popularly distorted to the point that evil was promoted in the name of God. He quickly pointed out how much more powerful goodness is in human lives than evil.

What did Jesus think was dishonorable about the practice of oaths in His day as a way of guaranteeing promises? (Matt. 5:33–36)

. . . .

. . . .

In what way does a simple "yes" or "no" approach to promises overcome the evils of a shaky system of oaths and vows?

. . . .

. . . .

CONSIDER THIS

Read the *WILSB* feature "An Eye for an Eye" (Matt. 5:38–42). "In this part of the Sermon on the Mount, the Lord is addressing the issue of justice. He was alluding to the Old Testament Law dealing with *public* vengeance."

How can the Old Testament standard "an eye for an eye" become a pretext for evil? (Matt. 5:38)

. . . .

. . . .

How do you think Jesus would have you overcome evil with good in response to each of these? (Matt. 5:39–42)

◆ An insult

. . . .

. . . .

◆ A lawsuit

. . . .

. . . .

◆ Unreasonable authority

. . . .

. . . .

◆ A request for a loan

. . . .

. . . .

Matthew 5:38–42 may be the most difficult part of the Sermon on the Mount to apply to life. Circle the letter of the following statement that you think best captures the point Jesus was making.

a. These are ideals that can't be applied to actual life situations. Their very impracticality reminds us how difficult true spirituality is.

b. Turn the other cheek once; then clobber the guy if he hits you again.

c. Respond to every personal insult and demand with as much generosity as God's love allows.

d. Let evil people abuse you freely. God will convict them of evil by means of your suffering.

e. Don't seek personal revenge; leave it up to the established judicial system.

The Old Testament never suggested hating your enemies. How do you think the idea of loving your neighbors (see Lev. 19:18) could get twisted to imply hating your enemies? (Matt. 5:43)

. . . .

. . . .

What less-than-admirable groups today love their friends who love them back? (see Matt. 5:46, 47)

. . . .

. . . .

In your life, how have you observed that God is kind to the unjust and wicked as well as to good people? (see Matt. 5:45)

. . . .

. . . .

Who would you identify as the "enemies" in your life—people who dislike you or who frustrate your plans?

. . . .

. . . .

In practical terms how can you love and bless these "enemies"? (see Matt. 5:44)

. . . .

. . . .

◆ REVOLT AGAINST HYPOCRISY ◆

(Matthew 6:1–18)

The three great acts of piety in first-century Judaism were almsgiving, prayer, and fasting.[2] Jesus expected His disciples to express their devotion to Him in similar practices, but He wanted the attitudes of their hearts to be right. Jesus hated few things more than hypocrisy in any of its forms.

What did Jesus identify as the great danger to avoid in charitable giving? (Matt. 6:1, 2)

In what sense do hypocritical givers receive all their reward at the time of their donations? (Matt. 6:1, 2)

How did Jesus teach His followers to make charitable donations? (Matt. 6:3, 4)

What do you think are the immediate and ultimate rewards of properly motivated giving? (Matt. 6:4)

CONSIDER THIS

Read the *WILSB* feature "Anonymous Donors" (Matt. 6:1–4). "As any fund-raiser knows, one of the biggest motivations for people who give large gifts is the prestige that results. Jesus questioned that spirit of giving."

How does giving anonymously to charitable causes bypass the spiritual dangers Jesus condemned in Matt. 6:1, 2?

What do you need to do to maintain humility when your giving is known about by others who commend you for it?

What pitfalls of prayer did Jesus warn His disciples about? (Matt. 6:5, 7)

. . . .

. . . .

How did Jesus recommend avoiding these pitfalls? (Matt. 6:6, 8)

. . . .

. . . .

Jesus extolled secret, individual praying (Matt. 6:6), but then gave a model prayer designed for group use (Matt. 6:9–13). How does this model prayer help you resist the hypocritical impulses of prideful praying?

. . . .

. . . .

The Lord's Prayer divides into halves. What is the subject of each half?

◆ Vv. 9, 10

. . . .

. . . .

◆ Vv. 11–13

. . . .

. . . .

What does it mean to you to be able to call God your Father? (Matt. 6:9)

. . . .

. . . .

How can you call attention to the holiness of God's name? (Matt. 6:9)

. . . .

. . . .

How can you advance the reign of God on earth? (Matt. 6:10)

. . . .

. . . .

When you ask God for your daily bread, what do you have in mind that you need or want? (Matt. 6:11)

. . . .

. . . .

How does your ability to forgive the offenses of others affect your ability to accept the forgiveness God extends to you? (Matt. 6:12)

. . . .

. . . .

What help do you expect from your heavenly Father as you resist temptation and the tempter? (Matt. 6:13)

. . . .

. . . .

Jesus reinforced the idea in the Lord's Prayer that our ability to receive God's forgiveness for our sins relates to our willingness to extend forgiveness to those who sin against us (Matt. 6:14, 15). Circle the letter of the following statement that best captures the meaning of this important, repeated teaching.

a. Neither a borrower nor a lender be. Debt is sinful.

b. God forgives my sins to the same extent that I forgive the offenses of others against me.

c. I have to forgive others completely before God will forgive me.

d. When I truly repent of my sins against God, I recognize how minor the offenses of others against me are and forgive them.

e. I can't repent of my sins against God until I let go of the offenses of others against me.

1. William Shakespeare, *The Merchant of Venice,* IV, i, 195–197.
2. D. A. Carson, 162.

LESSON 4

A Revolution in Values

Matthew 6:19—7:29

According to Greek mythology, Midas was ruling as king of Phrygia in Asia Minor when he did a favor for a god. The god rewarded King Midas with the power to turn anything to gold at a touch. At first the king was thrilled and created an instant fortune in gold from objects of little value.

The point of the myth is that true value is a deceptive quality. Gold is valuable when it can be "turned into" food, clothing, shelter, and endless luxuries. But when all of the needs and desires of life turned at Midas' slightest touch to cold, hard gold, gold was worse than worthless to him. It threatened to become lethal.

At this point the god reappeared and sent Midas to wash away his golden curse in the river Pactolus. The grateful king returned to his palace with a new appreciation of the value of the people and the ordinary pleasures of life that made him a good and honest man. Meanwhile, the Pactolus forever after washed golden sand down from the mountains.

In the wilderness the devil attempted to confuse Jesus by switching around the price tags on the important components of His life (Matt. 4:1–11). After each temptation, Jesus pointed the devil to the law of God as the standard for measuring the value of all things. Later in the Sermon on the Mount, the tender Messiah used His revolutionary authority as the One who fulfilled the Law and the Prophets to identify the chief treasures of life.

Treasure What Lasts

(Matthew 6:19–34)

In this section Jesus used a series of contrasts to illustrate the importance of enduring values. It's easy to pick out the enduring item in each contrasted set, but ironically the temporary choice is the one people usually make. These teachings are practical and necessary for everyone who wants to follow Jesus.

Why is treasure in heaven more valuable than treasure on earth? (Matt. 6:19–21)

. . . .

. . . .

What do you think it means to have a good "eye" that fills your life with light and a bad "eye" that fills your life with darkness? (Matt. 6:22, 23)

. . . .

. . . .

What makes a bad "eye" and a darkened life attractive to so many people in the short run but deadly in the long run?

. . . .

. . . .

Behind the choice of a life treasure and a life vision is the more fundamental choice of a life master. Why are the options of serving God or mammon (material wealth) mutually exclusive? (Matt. 6:24)

. . . .

. . . .

How did Jesus clarify His command not to worry about the necessities of life by each of these illustrations?

◆ The birds of the air (Matt. 6:26, 27)

. . . .

. . . .

◆ The lilies of the field (Matt. 6:28–30)

. . . .

. . . .

◆ The ignorant pagans (Matt. 6:31, 32)

. . . .

. . . .

What did Jesus present as the enduring alternative to worrying about the fleeting necessities of life? (Matt. 6:33, 34)

. . . .

. . . .

How will the choices we make about treasure, vision, and master (Matt. 6:19–24) affect whether we invest our life worrying about necessities or seeking God's kingdom (vv. 33, 34)?

. . . .

. . . .

CONSIDER THIS

Read the *Word in Life™ Study Bible (WILSB)* feature "Don't Worry!" (Matt. 6:19–34). "But Jesus urged us to stop worrying about things so that they dominate our lives and values. . . . Instead, we need to redirect our focus onto God's kingdom and righteousness."

God feeds the birds in your backyard (Matt. 6:26), but if you watch them you'll notice that they spend a lot of time and energy gathering up the grub He provides. But you won't find a neurotic in the flock. By what means does God provide the necessities of life for you?

. . . .

. . . .

What are you inclined to worry about with regard to the necessities of your life?

. . . .

. . . .

How is your commitment to accepting the reign of God in your life and advancing His reign into other lives hampered by your anxiety about daily needs?

. . . .

. . . .

What's the most important practical step you could take to focus more intently on the kingdom and righteousness of God?

. . . .

. . . .

◆ TREASURE WHAT'S FAIR ◆

(Matthew 7:1–12)

The tender Messiah never wanted His disciples to become self-righteous and judgmental. True righteousness begins with the revolutionary humility reflected in the Beatitudes (Matt. 5:3–10) and ends with the Golden Rule (7:12). One of the important ways in which the righteousness of the kingdom of God exceeds the righteousness of the scribes and Pharisees (5:20) is that it is fair and nonjudgmental.

CONSIDER THIS

Read the *WILSB* feature "Judge Not!" (Matt. 7:1). "What was Jesus calling for when He ordered His followers to 'judge not' " (v. 1)?

Actually Jesus was saying that we shouldn't judge anyone unless we are prepared to be judged as well (Matt. 7:1). By what standard should we expect to be judged, both in this life and in the judgment of the last days? (Matt. 7:2)

. . . .

. . . .

What does Jesus' illustration of the speck and the plank say about how to evaluate spiritual needs? (Matt. 7:3–5)

. . . .

. . . .

What factors should you take into account when you need to evaluate another person's character or performance?

. . . .

. . . .

If Matthew 7:1–5 speaks about the spiritual dangers of judgmentalism, verse 6 warns against the opposite error—lack of discernment. What kind of people could be compared to dogs that would like to tear you to pieces?

. . . .

. . . .

What kind of people could be compared to swine who trample their food in the mud? (Matt. 7:6)

. . . .

. . . .

What's been entrusted to you that you don't think you should share with these two groups of people?

. . . .

. . . .

While Jesus taught His followers to treat people fairly, He assured them that His Father would treat them fairly too (Matt 7:7–11). What does the progression in the verbs "ask," "seek," and "knock" (vv. 7, 8) suggest about the attitude we should bring to praying about the kingdom of God (6:9–13)?

. . . .

. . . .

What does the example of the kindness of human fathers suggest about God's approach to answering prayer? (Matt. 7:9–11)

. . . .

. . . .

Rate your confidence in God's interest in answering your prayers by circling the appropriate number on the following scale.

1	2	3	4	5	6	7	8	9	10
HE WON'T HEAR ME			HE MIGHT HEAR ME			HE OFTEN HEARS ME		HE ALWAYS HEARS ME	

Circle the letter(s) of the following statement(s) that reflect doubts about answered prayer with which you struggle.

a. I can't believe God cares about what happens in the details of my everyday life.

b. It seems as though my prayers are usually unanswered.

c. I'm not sure my life measures up to what God expects of someone who gets prayers answered.

d. I don't think I pray often enough or earnestly enough for God to pay attention to my prayers.

e. I think God's already decided what's going to happen and my prayers aren't important enough to change things.

In twenty-five words or less, paraphrase the Golden Rule (Matt. 7:12) in language common to your job, school, or family.

. . . .

. . . .

The Golden Rule isn't a statement of enlightened self-interest, such as "Honesty is the best policy."[1] Jesus gave it as a summary of "the Law and the Prophets" (Matt. 7:12). What difference does it make to you that the Golden

Rule is a summary of the righteousness of God's kingdom rather than advice about how to get what you want?

. . . .

. . . .

CONSIDER THIS

Read the *WILSB* feature "Quote Unquote" (Matt. 7:12). Martin Luther said about the tools and merchandise of working people, "All this is continually crying out to you: `Friend use me in your relations with your neighbor just as you would want your neighbor to use his property in relations with you.'"

How does the golden rule apply to your workplace, classroom, or homemaking?

. . . .

. . . .

◆ Treasure True Obedience ◆

(Matthew 7:13–29)

As Jesus approached the end of the Sermon on the Mount, He issued a series of challenges to His listeners to live according to the righteousness of the kingdom of God. These challenges are as compelling today as they were two thousand years ago.

In terms of the Sermon on the Mount, what do you think Jesus had in mind when He spoke of the two gates and roads?

◆ The wide gate and broad way (Matt. 7:13)

. . . .

. . . .

◆ The narrow gate and difficult way (Matt. 7:14)

. . . .

. . . .

What do you think are the greatest hindrances to people today choosing the narrow gate and difficult way?

. . . .

. . . .

How did the Lord attract and challenge you to enter the narrow gate and difficult way?

. . . .

. . . .

In terms of the Sermon on the Mount, what do you think Jesus had in mind when He spoke of two trees and their fruit? (Matt. 7:16–20)

◆ A good tree with good fruit

. . . .

. . . .

◆ A bad tree with bad fruit

. . . .

. . . .

In your opinion, who are the "false prophets," or teachers, that Christians need to be aware of today? What are the bad fruit of their lives that give them away?

. . . .

. . . .

Who among your Christian friends impresses you as a good tree bearing good fruit? Why?

. . . .

. . . .

Matthew 7:21–23 describes false followers of the kingdom. Perhaps they are disciples of the false teachers of verses 15–20.[2] How do you think it's possible for people to spend all of their time and energy in sincere and impressive religious activity and still be excluded from the kingdom of heaven? (Matt. 7:21–23)

. . . .

. . . .

In terms of the Sermon on the Mount, what did Jesus have in mind when He spoke of two builders and their houses?

◆ The man who built on the rock (Matt. 7:24, 25)

. . . .

. . . .

◆ The man who built on the sand (Matt. 7:26, 27)

. . . .

. . . .

As you contemplate your life in relationship to Jesus and His teaching, how is your life established securely and enduringly?

◆ For time

. . . .

. . . .

◆ For eternity

. . . .

. . . .

CONSIDER THIS

Read the *WILSB* feature "Jesus' Authority" (Matt. 7:29). "While [the scribes] held *positions* of authority, Jesus was a *person* of authority." Because all of the Law and Prophets found their fulfillment in Jesus, He had the authority to teach them creatively.

Give an example of a time when the Word of God absolutely astonished you in your devotions, a sermon, a Bible study, etc.

. . . .

. . . .

Give an example of an incident in which you strongly sensed the authority of Christ directing you to obey Him.

. . . .

. . . .

1. D. A. Carson, 188.
2. Ibid., 192.

The Tender King's Revolutionary Discipleship

Matthew 8:1—16:28

In the Sermon on the Mount the tender Messiah taught, "Whoever hears these sayings of Mine, and does them, I will liken him to a wise man who built his house on the rock" (Matt. 7:24). In Matthew 8—16, Jesus prepared His disciples to be the kind of wise men the Sermon on the Mount talked about.

This section of Matthew includes many of Jesus' miracles and parables that illustrate the authority and character of the kingdom of heaven. It also recounts the rise and intensity of opposition to anyone who lives as a citizen of the kingdom of heaven and announces that kingdom to others. It ends with the revolutionary assurance that the gates of hell cannot prevail against the united disciples of the Lord Jesus (16:18).

LESSON 7

No Ordinary Power

Matthew 8:1—10:42

Hank Morgan superintended a munitions factory in Connecticut when he was hit over the head during a quarrel with a worker and woke up as A Connecticut Yankee in King Arthur's Court.[1] *Mark Twain portrayed Hank as a nineteenth-century American entrepreneur who set out to enlighten and control the residents of Camelot and all of sixth-century England.*

Before Hank could introduce the wonders of the industrialized world, the Connecticut Yankee needed to convince King Arthur, Merlin, and the general populace that they should listen to him. He predicted an eclipse and won respect as a sage. He used his knowledge of technology to introduce railroads, steamships, telephones, and mass-produced goods into medieval England.

At first Hank kept his technological revolution a secret. Only a select group in Camelot knew his powers and his knowledge. But when the ingenious Yankee thought the time was right, he took his industrial message to the whole nation. Everyone was amazed by Hank Morgan. Many became avid fans; others became bitter enemies.

A Connecticut Yankee in King Arthur's Court *draws various reactions from literary critics. Morgan is more interested in profit than in people, but he was like Jesus in one regard: the Connecticut Yankee entered a world that did not know him and he revealed who he was by what he could do and by training others to spread the word. Hank Morgan couldn't really deliver on the revolutionary promises he made King Arthur, but the tender Messiah has delivered on all of His.*

◆ Power Over Things ◆

(Matthew 8:1–34)

As Jesus revealed His power to His disciples, He did it from the lesser to the greater, the more obvious to the less obvious. He showed them first His authority in the physical realm—control of disease, natural phenomena, and demonic activity. Only then would He move to the invisible spiritual realm and deal with sin and its consequences.

FOR YOUR INFO

Read the *Word in Life™ Study Bible (WILSB)* feature "Leprosy" (Matt. 8:2). "Any contact would defile the person who touched a leper. . . . Jesus intentionally healed lepers as a sign to vindicate His ministry."

Why do you think Jesus began expressing His power by touching a leper? (Matt. 8:1–4)

. . . .

. . . .

What kinds of people do you prefer to avoid? How might Jesus want you to "touch" them?

. . . .

. . . .

How was Jesus' exercise of power to heal the centurion's servant different from that which healed the leper? (Matt. 8:5–13)

. . . .

. . . .

Why did Jesus commend the faith of the centurion, when He did not commend the faith of the leper? (Matt. 8:10–12)

. . . .

. . . .

CONSIDER THIS

Read the *WILSB* feature "Under Authority" (Matt. 8:5–13). "The centurion's faith was marvelous because it was invested in the right person—Jesus. Leadership based on blind faith, either in others or in a system, is foolhardy."

Which of the leadership traits expressed by the centurion do you most want to be true of you? Why?

. . . .

. . . .

What is the greatest difficulty you have dealing with authority? How does this affect your relationship with Christ?

. . . .

. . . .

CONSIDER THIS

Read the *WILSB* feature "Jesus' Global Connections" (Matt. 8:10). "While Matthew's Gospel portrays Jesus in terms of His Jewish roots, it also shows that Jesus is an international Savior, a Messiah for the whole world."

Why would Matthew stress Jesus' contacts with Gentiles in a gospel oriented toward Jewish readers?

. . . .

. . . .

Why do you think Jesus tended to gravitate toward the outcasts within Jewish society?

. . . .

. . . .

CONSIDER THIS

Read the *WILSB* feature "A Surprise in Peter's Household" (Matt. 8:14, 15). "The Lord's compassion extended to widowed mothers-in-law even when He was a house guest!"

What additional aspects of the power of Jesus were revealed by His many healings at Peter's house? (Matt. 8:14, 15)

. . . .

. . . .

When have you been willing to inconvenience yourself to meet the needs of others?

. . . .

. . . .

What did Jesus try to teach two would-be followers about counting the cost of discipleship? (Matt. 8:18–22)

. . . .

. . . .

CONSIDER THIS

Read the *WILSB* feature "Jesus—A Homeless Man?" (Matt. 8:20). "Jesus was born poor and lived poor. His comment in v. 20 even suggests that He was homeless."

What trapping of material security would be hardest for you to give up?

. . . .

. . . .

How does material security tend to affect your dependence on the power of Christ?

. . . .

. . . .

What did Jesus reveal about His physical authority by calming the storm on the Sea of Galilee? (Matt. 8:23–27)

. . . .

. . . .

Why do you suppose the disciples were frightened by Jesus' control of nature but not by His earlier control of disease?

. . . .

. . . .

The people along the lake shore were more bothered by the loss of the swine than the healing of the demoniacs (Matt. 8:33, 34). When have you seen someone reject Jesus because they feared accepting His authority would cost them something?

. . . .

. . . .

What sin has Jesus abolished from your life as decisively as He cast the demons from the two demoniacs?

. . . .

. . . .

◆ Power Over Sin ◆

(Matthew 9:1–38)

If the lesser but more obvious demonstration of Jesus' power involved physical matters, the greater but invisible expressions of power happened in the spiritual realm. The more spectacular physical miracles prepared people to accept Jesus' spiritual pronouncements.

What do you suppose the paralytic and his friends had faith that Jesus would do? (Matt. 9:1, 2)

. . . .

. . . .

Why did Jesus respond to the faith of the paralytic by forgiving his sins before healing him physically? (Matt. 9:2)

. . . .

. . . .

Why were there different responses to Jesus' forgiving and healing the paralytic? (Matt. 9:4–8)

. . . .

. . . .

CONSIDER THIS

Read the *WILSB* feature "The Power of Forgiveness" (Matt. 9:4–8). "Forgiveness is as powerful and liberating as the healing of a paralytic."

When has someone forgiven you and set you free from a burden of guilt?

. . . .

. . . .

When have you forgiven someone and released them from a burden of guilt?

. . . .

. . . .

CONSIDER THIS

Read the *WILSB* feature "Who Were Those Tax Collectors?" (Matt. 9:10). "They often gathered more than the government required and pocketed the excess amount—a practice that John the Baptist specifically preached against."

The Pharisees avoided contact with lepers and sinners to avoid physical and spiritual defilement. Jesus made contact with lepers (Matt. 8:3) and sinners (9:10) to heal and forgive. How did Jesus explain Himself and challenge the Pharisees? (Matt. 9:12, 13)

. . . .

. . . .

How does the spiritual power Jesus brings into every situation affect everyone and everything around Him? (Matt. 9:14–17)

. . . .

. . . .

In your life or in your church, what old ways of doing things are being stretched by the ever-new spiritual energy of Jesus?

. . . .

. . . .

CONSIDER THIS

Read the *WILSB* feature "The Hemorrhaging Woman" (Matt. 9:20–22). "So she approached [Jesus], breaking a rule that made it an unclean person's responsibility to keep away from others. In desperation, she reached out and touched Jesus."

What did Jesus show about His power to deal with the needs of a person's spirit by the way He interacted with the hemorrhaging woman? (Matt. 9:20–22)

. . . .

. . . .

What does each of these features of the story of the resurrection of the little girl suggest about Jesus' spiritual authority?

◆ A synagogue ruler bowed to Jesus (Matt. 9:18)

. . . .

. . . .

◆ The mourners mocked Jesus (Matt. 9:23, 24)

. . . .

. . . .

◆ Jesus defeated death (Matt. 9:25)

. . . .

. . . .

What is shown about Jesus' spiritual authority when He connected His healing of the blind men to their faith? (Matt. 9:27–31)

. . . .

. . . .

Why do you think the Pharisees characterized the spiritual power of Jesus as satanic in origin? (Matt. 9:32–34)

. . . .

. . . .

What are the qualities of Jesus' spiritual authority that make the satanic charge ludicrous? (Matt. 9:35–38)

. . . .

. . . .

CONSIDER THIS

Read the *WILSB* feature "Jesus—A City Preacher" (Matt. 9:35). "So as Jesus carried out His ministry, He focused on the urban centers of Palestine. . . . This brought Him into contact with a greater number and wider variety of people."

Circle the letter of the statement that best represents your attitude toward cities.

a. I won't live in a city and don't understand anyone who wants to.

b. I live in a city because I have to, but I'd like to escape it.

c. I appreciate cities as places for shopping and employment, but I live outside and commute.

d. I find urban life professionally and culturally stimulating.

e. I think cities are the key to the future. I want to help shape that future.

What kinds of ministries do you think the church of Jesus Christ needs in the hearts of the major cities of the country?

. . . .

. . . .

CONSIDER THIS

Read the *WILSB* feature "What It Means To Be Like Jesus #7" (Matt. 8:1—9:38). "If we want to be like Jesus, we need to befriend those who are weak, under oppression, or without Christ."

To be like Jesus, who should you be befriending in each of these categories?

◆ Someone weak

. . . .

. . . .

◆ Someone oppressed

. . . .

. . . .

◆ Someone without Christ

. . . .

. . . .

◆ Power to Share ◆

(Matthew 10:1–15)

Hank Morgan often displayed his technological powers to astonish people; Jesus never did. The Connecticut Yankee didn't want to share his know-how lest he lose his advantage; Jesus wanted to spread His authority to share with many the advantages of the kingdom of heaven.

CONSIDER THIS

Read the *WILSB* features "What It Means To Be Like Jesus #8" (Matt. 10:1–42) and "The Twelve" (10:2). "If we want to be like Him, we will share the joys and risks of working together with our brothers and sisters."

Why do you think Jesus delegated physical and spiritual authority to His disciples along with the message of the kingdom?

. . . .

. . . .

Circle the number on the scale that represents your ability to delegate work to coworkers.

1	2	3	4	5	6	7	8	9	10
RATHER DO IT MYSELF			HOVERING BOSS			IT'S YOURS, GOOD LUCK		TRAINING, CONFIDENCE, PRAISE	

Identify some of the tasks the Lord has delegated to you during your Christian life, and tell how He prepared you for them.

. . . .

. . . .

At this point in His ministry, why do you think Jesus restricted His disciples to the cities and towns of Israel in announcing the kingdom of heaven? (Matt. 10:5, 6)

. . . .

. . . .

What basic principles of ministry would you draw from Jesus' instruction to His disciples for the particular kingdom tour described in Matthew 10:5–15?

. . . .

. . . .

◆ Power For You ◆

(Matthew 10:16–42)

The first part of Jesus' message to His disciples seems to be addressed primarily to the immediate historical situation. The longer, latter portion seems to apply more generally to His followers at all times. While the Twelve were promised extraordinary powers, all of us are promised persecutions and divine assistance to face them.

How will persecution against disciples of Jesus manifest itself? (Matt. 10:17–22)

. . . .

. . . .

How did Jesus instruct His disciples to find divine assistance during persecution? (Matt. 10:16, 19)

. . . .

. . . .

What did Jesus teach His disciples about the following subjects to prepare them for ministry?

◆ Fear (Matt. 10:24–31)

. . . .

. . . .

◆ Confession (Matt. 10:32, 33)

. . . .

. . . .

◆ Priorities (Matt. 10:34–39)

. . . .

. . . .

◆ Response (Matt. 10:40–42)

. . . .

. . . .

Circle the letter or the statement that best captures your response to Jesus' training of His disciples for witness.

a. I'm going to devote myself to prayer and meditation about my fearfulness.

b. I can't stand the thought of division in my family because of my faith in Christ. That can't be right.

c. I'm encouraged to know that there will be special grace from God to cope with serious persecution, if it should ever come to that.

d. I'm greatly challenged by the prospect of becoming more and more like Jesus.

e. I'm concerned that I may deny Christ before people and be denied by Him in heaven.

f. Other

. . . .

. . . .

1. Samuel L. Clemens, *A Connecticut Yankee in King Arthur's Court* (New York: Charles L. Webster and Company, 1889).

LESSON 6

Drawing a Line in the Sand

Matthew 11:1—13:52

Francisco Pizarro came to the New World from Spain seeking adventure. He accompanied Balboa on his famous expedition that discovered the Pacific Ocean in 1513. Then Pizarro settled down in Panama and made his fortune as a cattle rancher. But ranching was too tame.

Pizarro dreamed of conquering and plundering the fabled Inca empire in South America. He plotted and schemed off and on for seven years with a fortune hunter and a priest about finding the riches of the Incas. Finally in 1531 Pizarro got the approval of the King of Spain and launched a serious expedition.

Pizarro gathered with his three brothers and 180 mercenaries on a Pacific beach in preparation for sailing for the coast of Peru. "Drawing his sword he traced a line in the sand from East to West. Then, turning toward the South, 'Friends and Comrades!' he said, 'on that side are toil, hunger, nakedness, the drenching storm, desertion, and death; on this side ease and pleasure. There lies Peru with its riches; here, Panama and its poverty. Choose, each man, what best becomes a brave Castilian. For my part, I go to the South.' So saying he stepped across the line."[1]

Pizarro's men crossed his line in the sand to join him in bloody conquest and fabulous wealth. The revolutionary life and teaching of Jesus also amounted to a line in the sand. As His ministry developed, more and more men and women crossed over into serious discipleship. At the same time a growing number consciously refused to cross that line. These conscious rejectors formed the nucleus of a growing body of active opponents to Jesus.

The Line Between Bad and Good "Children"

(Matthew 11:1–30)

Jesus enjoyed great popularity in the early days of His public ministry, but He knew it would not last. He enjoyed comparing adults to children, so it was natural for Him to liken His opponents as well as His supporters to groups of children everyone has seen at one time or another. Be sure you're on the "good" side of this line.

CONSIDER THIS

Read the *Word in Life™ Study Bible (WILSB)* feature "Some Surprising Evidence" (Matt. 11:2–6). "Like John, observers are asking whether those of us who claim to be Christ's followers are truly of God, or whether they should look elsewhere." Even John had expected the Messiah to act differently than Jesus did.

Jesus didn't match popular expectations of the Messiah. How did His works align with biblical predictions about the Messiah? (Matt. 11:4–6)

. . . .

. . . .

How did Jesus evaluate John the Baptist as His forerunner? (Matt. 11:7–15)

. . . .

. . . .

What can you learn about witnessing for Christ from the examples of these two?

◆ Jesus (Matt. 11:1–6)

. . . .

. . . .

◆ John the Baptist (Matt. 11:7–12)

. . . .

. . . .

Why did Jesus compare the general public of His day to children who were never satisfied? (Matt. 11:16–19)

. . . .

. . . .

Apparently, some of the worst "children" Jesus and His disciples encountered in their preaching were in the towns along the northern end of the Sea of Galilee. Capernaum was Jesus' base of operations, and Bethsaida was the hometown of Peter and Andrew as well as James and John. Chorazin was a couple of miles inland. How had they behaved as bad children? (Matt. 11:20–24)

. . . .

. . . .

How can people today behave like these same "bad children"?

. . . .

. . . .

Jesus rejoiced that His Father had revealed the great truths of the kingdom of heaven "to babes" (Matt. 11:25)—to good children. What characterizes the "good children" to whom the Father reveals deep spiritual truths? (Matt. 11:25–30)

The Pharisees had burdened the people of Jesus' day with numerous traditions and yoked them to guilt. What are today's heavy burdens and uncomfortable yokes that should cause people to desire Jesus' help?

◆ BETWEEN BAD AND GOOD "LAWS" ◆

(Matthew 12:1–21)

Once the Jewish leaders realized that a portion of the population was disillusioned with Jesus' presentation of the kingdom of heaven, they tried to show He was a lawbreaker. Pharisaic traditions specified thirty-nine unlawful Sabbath activities, including shelling and eating grain.[1] Jesus used two Old Testament examples to illustrate that the Pharisees used the Law wrongly. What did each example imply about Jesus and the Law?

◆ David (Matt. 12:3, 4)

◆ The priests (Matt. 12:5–7)

How did Jesus argue as the fulfiller of the Law that the Pharisees practiced bad law while He practiced good law? (Matt: 12:9–13)

A CLOSER LOOK

Read the *WILSB* feature "Political Intrigue" (Matt. 12:14). "They were concerned that [Jesus'] popularity might have political repercussions, drawing

Roman troops to the area and causing the loss of what little independence the nation had."

What did the Pharisees do when they could not discredit Jesus in confrontations over their specialty, the Law? (Matt. 12:14)

. . . .

. . . .

How did Jesus' response to the plot of the Pharisees fulfill the "good Law" about the Messiah as the Suffering Servant? (Matt. 12:15–21)

. . . .

. . . .

How can the Pharisaic attitude of "bad law" have a negative effect on a Christian or a church trying to serve Christ?

. . . .

. . . .

How can you be sure you are following the Christlike attitude of "good law" in your approach to the Bible and life?

. . . .

. . . .

◆ Between Bad and Good "Spirits" ◆

(Matthew 12:22–50)

It was inevitable that the conflict between Jesus and the Pharisees would boil down to their basic motivations. The Pharisees went for broke with an outrageous charge against the tender Messiah. In turn, Jesus made some revolutionary predictions about the future of those who insist on opposing the purposes of God.

How did the Pharisees explain Jesus' power over evil spirits? (Matt. 12:22–24)

. . . .

. . . .

What inconsistencies did Jesus point out about the reasoning of the Pharisees concerning His power over demons? (Matt. 12:25–30)

. . . .

. . . .

CONSIDER THIS

Read the *WILSB* feature "No Forgiveness!" (Matt. 12:31, 32). "It is possible to willfully place oneself beyond the grace of God—to persist in rebellion and sin and resist His call to repentance."

How had the Pharisees been blaspheming Jesus? (Matt. 12:1–24)

How did they blaspheme the Holy Spirit? (Matt. 12:24)

How do you think blaspheming the Holy Spirit puts a person beyond hope of repentance, faith, and forgiveness?

Jesus charged the Pharisees with showing their "bad spirit" through their words (Matt. 12:33–37). True disciples show their "good spirit" the same way. Give an example of a time when you picked up from a new acquaintance's speech that that person was controlled by sin.

Give an example of when you realized from a new acquaintance's speech that that person spoke from a good heart.

When the scribes and Pharisees demanded a sign from Jesus as they searched frantically for a way to discredit Him, Jesus refused and used three Old Testament examples to support His refusal (Matt. 12:39–42). What do you think each of the biblical examples added to Jesus' refusal to perform tricks?

- ◆ Jonah (Matt. 12:39, 40)

- ◆ People of Nineveh (Matt. 12:41)

◆ The queen of the South (Matt. 12:42)

. . . .

. . . .

Jesus was doing His utmost to break the power of evil over His generation. What did He predict would happen if they continued to reject Him and His message? (Matt. 12:43–45)

. . . .

. . . .

CONSIDER THIS

Read the *WILSB* feature "Turning Back Is Awful" (Matt. 12:43–45). "Do you intend to overcome evil? If so, make sure to replace it with good or else, as Jesus warns, the evil may return with its friends."

Rate yourself on the following scale on how well you follow through on your intentions to root out evil from your life.

1	2	3	4	5	6	7	8	9	10
NO FOLLOW THROUGH			LITTLE FOLLOW THROUGH			SOME FOLLOW THROUGH			STRONG FOLLOW THROUGH

Identify the sinful habit or pattern of life that you have had the greatest difficulty getting rid of.

. . . .

. . . .

What good practices do you need to build into your life in its place by the help and grace of the Holy Spirit of God?

. . . .

. . . .

Jesus identified His spiritual family as "whoever does the will of My Father in heaven" (Matt. 12:50). How does this family relationship relate to whether one has a "good" or "bad" spirit?

. . . .

. . . .

◆ BETWEEN BAD AND GOOD "SOILS" ◆

(Matthew 13:1–23)

Matthew 13 contains the greatest concentration of the parables of Jesus found in the Gospels. Jesus identified the first of these parables—the parable of the soils—as foundational to all of the others.

Describe the setting in which Jesus told His parables. (Matt. 13:1, 2)

. . . .

. . . .

What happened to the seed sown on each of the four soils?

◆ Hard soil (Matt. 13:4)

. . . .

. . . .

◆ Shallow soil (Matt. 13:5, 6)

. . . .

. . . .

◆ Thorny soil (Matt. 13:7)

. . . .

. . . .

◆ Good soil (Matt. 13:8)

. . . .

. . . .

Circle the letter of the statement that best captures the genius of parables as a mass teaching method.

a. Parables annoyed the scribes and Pharisees because they preferred lectures to stories.

b. Parables made country people feel as smart as city people since the stories were taken from their way of life.

c. Parables are ordinary figures of speech that people of average intelligence understand right away.

d. Parables are so confusing that no one who doesn't have special spiritual insight can understand them .

e. Parables separate the spiritually interested from the spiritually disinterested. The interested will ask for further explanation.

Give the meaning of each of the soils in Jesus' foundational parable (Matt. 13:18–23). After each interpretation, give an example of an encounter with the Word of God when you have responded that way.

◆ Hard soil (Matt. 13:19)

◆ Example

◆ Shallow soil (Matt. 13:20, 21)

◆ Example

◆ Thorny soil (Matt. 13:22)

◆ Example

◆ Good soil (Matt. 13:23)

◆ Example

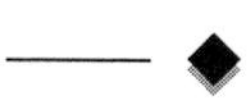 "BAD" AND "GOOD" ILLUSTRATED 

(Matthew 13:24–52)

The remaining six parables Jesus told illustrate revolutionary truths about the kingdom of heaven and opposition to it. One of these parables also is explained, and four of them group into pairs. All together the parables give a fascinating picture of the "good" kingdom opposed by "bad" enemies.

Read the parable of the wheat and the tares (Matt. 13:24–30). Don't read Jesus' later interpretation of it yet. Tares probably were darnel, a weed that initially looks like wheat. It does not form a head and at maturity is much shorter than wheat.[2] What seems to be the main point this story illustrates about the kingdom of heaven?

. . . .

. . . .

What is the main point about the kingdom of heaven in the parable of the mustard seed? (Matt. 13:31, 32)

. . . .

. . . .

What is the main point about the kingdom of heaven in the parable of leaven? (Matt. 13:33)

. . . .

. . . .

What is the difference in the way the mustard seed and leaven produce their effect? What do these two processes illustrate about the kingdom of heaven?

. . . .

. . . .

In response to a request from His disciples, Jesus gave a rather elaborate interpretation of the parable of the wheat and the tares (Matt. 13:36–43). What does the parable illustrate about the present and the future?

◆ The present

. . . .

. . . .

◆ The future

. . . .

. . . .

CONSIDER THIS

Read the *WILSB* feature "The Incomparable Value of the Kingdom" (Matt. 13:44–46). In the parable of the hidden treasure, a man finds something he wasn't looking for. In the parable of the priceless pearl, another man finds what he has looked for all his life. What do these parables tell about discovering the kingdom of heaven?

◆ The hidden treasure (Matt. 13:44)

. . . .

. . . .

◆ The priceless pearl (Matt. 13:45, 46)

. . . .

. . . .

What things does the parable of the dragnet illustrate about the kingdom of heaven in the last days (Matt. 13:47–50)? What does it add to the parable of the wheat and tares?

. . . .

. . . .

CONSIDER THIS

Read the *WILSB* features "Work-World Stories Describe the Kingdom" (Matt. 13:1) and "Treasures New and Old" (13:52). "As we confront situations, we can look back to the 'old' truths, the fundamental things that never change, and we can also discern how to apply biblical truth to new issues in ways that are fresh and alive."

What new things to shape your life and thought have you learned about the kingdom of heaven from these parables?

. . . .

. . . .

What old things about the kingdom that you already knew have you been reminded of by these parables to apply in fresh ways to your life and thought?

. . . .

. . . .

1. Craig S. Keener, *The IVP Bible Background Commentary: New Testament* (Downers Grove, IL: InterVarsity Press, 1993), 78.

2. *Ibid.*, 83.

LESSON 7

Choosing Sides in the Revolution

Matthew 13:53—16:28

In the early years of the fifteenth century, Henry V of England defeated the armies of Charles VI of France at Agincourt in Normandy. The direction of the Hundred Years' War turned decidedly in England's favor. France seemed destined to be an English province. But in 1429 Joan of Arc appeared before Charles VII and announced that God had appointed her to deliver France from the occupying enemy.

Within two months Joan broke the siege of Orléans. Then she led the young king through English lines into Reims for his official coronation. French morale rose from the dead, and the armies of Joan launched four more reckless assaults. All succeeded.

Not quite everyone loved Joan. Some theologians doubted the voices Joan had begun to hear at age thirteen. Other ecclesiastics frowned when Joan held her voices more authoritative than the church. When Joan lost to the English at Paris, she left 1,500 casualties on the field. The Maid of Orléans' support suddenly divided. Some soldiers "cursed her for thinking that a prayer could silence a gun; this had not been their experience. Some Frenchwomen, who had jealously waited for her first reverse, censured her for leading an assault on the feast of the Virgin's birth."[1]

Joan was captured, tried by the English, and burned at the stake. She became the symbol of French courage and resistance to tyranny. During her brief life powerful forces divided over whether to support or denounce her.

As soon as Jesus faced visible opposition, a division arose within the population of Judea and Galilee about Him. Support became more loyal and articulate. Hostility became more bitter and vocal. The wheat and tares of the kingdom of heaven began to become distinct (Matt. 13:24–26, 38).

Taking Offense

(Matthew 13:53—14:12)

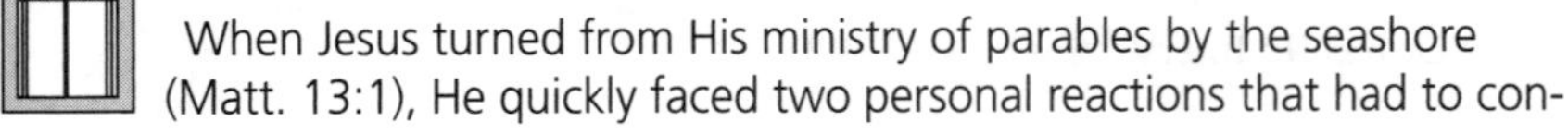

When Jesus turned from His ministry of parables by the seashore (Matt. 13:1), He quickly faced two personal reactions that had to concern Him. At the bottom of the social scale but close to the heart of Jesus, the hometown folks of Nazareth were offended by Him. At the top of the social scale but far removed from Jesus' circle of friends, Herod Antipas heard of Him and worried.

What was the reaction of the residents of Nazareth to Jesus when He taught in their synagogue? (Matt. 13:53–57)

. . . .

. . . .

How did Jesus respond to their familiarity? (Matt. 13:57, 58)

. . . .

. . . .

What happens to your spiritual life when you get overly familiar with Jesus and take Him for granted?

. . . .

. . . .

Herod Antipas, son of Herod the Great, ruled Galilee and Perea (the east bank of the Jordan) from 4 B.C. to A.D. 39. What was Herod's explanation for the powerful parables and miracles of Jesus? (Matt. 14:1, 2)

. . . .

. . . .

How many reasons can you find for Herod's guilty, superstitious conscience in Matthew 14:3–11?

. . . .

. . . .

Many people look for occult or mysterious explanations for major events. How does this tendency draw their attention away from what God is trying to teach them?

. . . .

. . . .

CONSIDER THIS

Read the *Word in Life™ Study Bible (WILSB)* feature "Hateful Herodias" (Matt. 14:3). Herodias's "choice, to use her daughter to work her vengeance on an innocent man, ranks among the worst" of the terrible but truthful tales in the Bible.

What do you think happens to the hearts of people like Herodias who destroy others to gratify their selfish desires?

. . . .

. . . .

In what kinds of situations do you need to resist the temptation to harm others for selfish ends?

. . . .

. . . .

◆ INTENSIFIED LOYALTY ◆

(Matthew 14:13–36)

When Jesus heard that Herod thought He was John the Baptist risen from the dead, He withdrew from the public eye to let things cool off (Matt. 14:13). For a time He devoted His attention to strengthening the loyalties of His close disciples.

Multitudes of curious Galileans followed Jesus when He tried to be alone with His disciples. What did the disciples conclude about their abilities and resources when Jesus challenged them to meet the needs of the multitude? (Matt. 14:14–17)

. . . .

. . . .

What did Jesus demonstrate about His abilities and resources when He fed the 5,000? (Matt. 14:18–21)

. . . .

. . . .

What lessons do you draw from the feeding of the 5,000 about the Lord's ability and interest in caring for you?

. . . .

. . . .

FOR YOUR INFO

Read the *WILSB* feature "Telling Time" (Matt. 14:25). The fourth watch would have been "near sunrise, indicating that the disciples had spent virtually the entire night struggling with the stormy conditions!"

What do you think the disciples of Jesus should have learned from each of these features of the episode on the Sea of Galilee? (Matt. 14:22–33)

◆ Alone against the wind

. . . .

. . . .

◆ Seeing Jesus walking on the water

. . . .

. . . .

◆ Peter trying to walk on water

. . . .

. . . .

◆ Jesus' charge that their faith was small

. . . .

. . . .

Give an example of a time when you felt you were about to sink below the waves of life and the Lord rescued you.

. . . .

. . . .

Gennesaret was a small, fertile plain on the northwest shore of the Sea of Galilee. What was the conclusion of Jesus' efforts to get out of the public eye? (Matt. 14:34–36)

. . . .

. . . .

◆ INTENSIFIED HATRED ◆

(Matthew 15:1–20)

While the loyalties of Jesus' disciples deepened because of further insights into His person and power, the hostility of His enemies also grew. The scribes and Pharisees believed they were the authoritative interpreters of the Law. Jesus knew He was the fulfillment of the Law (Matt. 5:17) and freely ignored Pharisaic traditions. They hated Him for that.

CONSIDER THIS

Read the *WILSB* feature "Tradition" (Matt. 15:1–3). "Believers in the workplace . . . are called upon to be both sustainers and breakers of tradition. There are no simple formulas to help one decide how to respond to tradition."

How did Jesus figure that the scribes and Pharisees were hypocrites for blaming His disciples for violating their tradition about hand washing? (Matt. 15:3–9)

. . . .

. . . .

What did Jesus, the fulfillment of the Law, say defiles a person? Why? (Matt. 15:10, 11, 16–20)

. . . .

. . . .

How did Jesus describe the Pharisees? Why? (Matt. 15:12–15)

. . . .

. . . .

Today, as in every age, some Christians want to make a list of behaviors that will defile a person who does them. What defiling heart attitudes do list-makers need to guard against in their attempts to guard purity?

. . . .

. . . .

◆ Loving the Unlovely ◆

(Matthew 15:21–39)

After His encounter with the scribes and Pharisees, Jesus took His disciples into Gentile territory in an attempt to find some privacy with them. Even there, people made demands on His time. Jesus had no time for the traditions of the Pharisees, but He could not ignore the needs of Gentiles who reached out to Him in faith.

Tyre and Sidon were commercial cities on the Mediterranean coast thirty to fifty miles northwest of Capernaum. Circle the letter of the following statement that you think best explains why Jesus was reluctant to heal the daughter of the Canaanite woman (Matt. 15:21–26).

a. He was testing her perseverance to see how strong her faith was.

b. He didn't want to deal with Gentiles because that phase of His ministry was strictly for Jews.

c. He delayed healing her daughter so He could use her faith as an example for His disciples who did not have faith that strong.

d. He was annoyed that she would disturb His privacy.

e. He asked her to acknowledge the priority of the Jews in this stage of His ministry before rewarding her faith.

The Canaanite woman respectfully persisted in her request for her daughter (Matt. 15:25, 27). Circle the number on the following scale which reflects the persistence with which you pray.

1	2	3	4	5	6	7	8	9	10
APOLOGETIC			"I HOPE, I HOPE,"			"I KNOW YOU MIGHT"		HOLY CHUTZPAH	

CONSIDER THIS

Read the *WILSB* feature "Jews, Gentiles, and Jesus" (Matt. 15:24). "Racism and ethnic hatred have never been God's desire. . . . Jesus repudiated such sin wherever He found it."

How can you follow Christ in responding to the racial or ethnic divisions in your community?

. . . .

. . . .

How can you follow Christ in responding to racial and ethnic divisions around the world?

. . . .

. . . .

The multitude in Matthew 15:29–31 was probably a Gentile gathering in the Decapolis east of the Sea of Galilee because "they glorified the God of Israel" (v. 31). Why do you think Jesus took time away from His disciples to heal this multitude of sick Gentiles?

. . . .

. . . .

The feeding of the 4,000 also occurred in the Gentile region of the Decapolis (see Mark 7:31—8:10). Why do you think Jesus fed this hungry Gentile audience (Matt. 15:32–38) in much the same way He fed the earlier Jewish one (14:13–21)?

. . . .

. . . .

Give an example of a time when you went out of your way to care for someone you didn't consider a priority in your life at the time. Why did you do it? What did the experience mean to you?

. . . .

. . . .

◆ Shades of Discernment ◆

(Matthew 16:1–20)

All of the gospels record the feeding of the 5,000—Jesus' presentation of Himself as the Shepherd who could meet the deepest needs of His flock. Those who understood the significance of this miracle (and the feeding of the 4,000 Gentiles) would know a great deal about the kingdom of heaven.

FOR YOUR INFO

Read the *WILSB* feature "Party Politics of Jesus' Day" (Matt. 16:1). The first attempt to discern the ministry of Jesus came from an unlikely alliance of Pharisees and Sadducees. What was Jesus' response to their request for a sign? (Matt.16:1–4)

. . . .

. . . .

Why do you think Jesus dismissed the Jewish leaders' request so abruptly?

. . . .

. . . .

Why do you think Jesus compared the doctrine of the Pharisees and Sadducees to yeast in bread dough? (Matt. 16:6, 12)

. . . .

. . . .

What do you think Jesus expected His disciples to have learned from the two miraculous feedings that should have helped them understand His meaning? (Matt. 16:8–11)

. . . .

. . . .

Caesarea Philippi was the chief city of the Decapolis (Matt. 16:13). Jesus quizzed His disciples about His identity while in the shadows of a town that honored the political lord of the earth—the Roman emperor. What kind of discernment did popular opinion show in trying to identify Jesus? (Matt. 16:13–15)

. . . .

. . . .

Why do you think Jesus said that Simon Peter's identification of Him as "the Christ, the Son of the living God" was a revelation from God? (Matt. 16:16, 17)

. . . .

. . . .

In what ways did Peter's confession of Jesus as the Messiah serve as the foundation for the church and the criterion for admission to or exclusion from it? (Matt. 16:18, 19)

. . . .

. . . .

CONSIDER THIS

Read the *WILSB* feature "The Gates of Hell" (Matt. 16:18). For Jesus' listeners, "the gates of Hades were not just a spiritual abstraction but actual forces of evil at work among human systems—the Roman government, for instance."

How do you perceive hell's "city hall" assailing the church today?

. . . .

. . . .

How do you think you should pray and behave in light of Jesus' teaching about "the gates of Hades"?

. . . .

. . . .

Shades of Ignorance

(Matthew 16:21–28)

In the first part of Matthew 16, Peter showed the greatest degree of discernment about Jesus and the kingdom of heaven. Unfortunately, in the final verses of the chapter he led the way in ignorance about the necessity for suffering to establish the kingdom.

Why do you think Jesus refrained from clearly predicting His death and resurrection until after Peter identified Him as the Messiah? (Matt. 16:21)

. . . .

. . . .

In Matthew 4:8–9 the devil offered Jesus rule of the world without suffering, and Jesus rebuked him sharply (v. 10). How does this help explain why Jesus compared Peter to Satan and questioned his discernment of "the things of God"? (Matt. 16:23)

. . . .

. . . .

Peter wanted Jesus to gain the world without suffering (Matt. 16:22). What did Jesus have to say about those who choose to be ignorant of the necessity of suffering? (Matt. 16:24–27)

. . . .

. . . .

What does it mean to you that Jesus asks you to carry your cross every day? (Matt. 16:24)

. . . .

. . . .

Circle the letters of the following statements that may explain what Jesus meant when He said some of His disciples would live to see Him come "in His kingdom" (Matt. 16:28).

a. The Transfiguration six days later revealed the glory of the future kingdom.

b. When Jesus rose from the dead, the disciples witnessed the victory over death that characterizes the kingdom.

c. At Pentecost the Holy Spirit indwelt the people of the new covenant and a visible expression of the kingdom.

d. Jesus referred to His reign in all forms based on the confession that Peter had made.

e. Jesus was prophesying of His second coming and using "some standing here" to represent all who would believe in the future through the disciples.

1. Will Durant, *The Reformation,* Vol. VI of *The Story of Civilization* (New York: Simon and Schuster, 1957), 84.

The Tender King's Revolutionary Faith

Matthew 17:1—25:46

It is possible to read Matthew and get the impression that this Gospel presents a Christian law as difficult to keep as the Law of Moses. Chapters 17—25 stress the centrality of faith on the part of the disciples of Jesus. Although Jesus didn't use the word, grace lies behind the major concepts of this portion of Matthew.

The ability to be a disciple comes through the grace of God, not individual effort or determination. The insight to understand the gospel comes through the grace of God. Safety in the future depends on the mercy and grace of God. All of this is implicit in the teaching of Jesus about childlike faith that longs for the full expression of the kingdom of heaven.

LESSON 7

20-20 Faith

Matthew 17:1—19:30

In The Lion, the Witch and the Wardrobe, *C. S. Lewis created the world of Narnia where a story of redemption unfolded that echoed the gospel accounts of Jesus' atonement.*[1] *Four children—brothers and sisters—discovered Narnia. Peter, the oldest, was thoughtful and courageous. Susan showed compassion and common sense. Edmund betrayed the others and learned the humility and strength of being forgiven. Little Lucy exhibited tenacious faith.*

It was Lucy who first stumbled into Narnia through an ancient wardrobe in the professor's rambling, mysterious country manor. The other three disbelieved Lucy's tale of a vast world of perpetual winter behind a row of fur coats inside the wardrobe. Peter reasoned with her, Susan humored her, and Edmund mocked her. Adults would have begun to doubt their fantastic story and concluded they had imagined it all, but Lucy never wavered in her confidence that Narnia was real.

Lucy's childlike faith led all of the children into wonderful Narnian adventures. In Matthew 17—19 Jesus appealed for that same childlike faith on the part of His disciples.

Spiritual Sight and Blindness

(Matthew 17:1–23)

Six days after predicting that some of His disciples would "see the Son of Man coming in His kingdom" (Matt. 16:28), Jesus took Peter, James, and John up on a high mountain and was transfigured before them (17:1, 2). What do you think Jesus' altered appearance would have meant to His disciples? (Matt. 17:1, 2)

. . . .

. . . .

Moses, the lawgiver and leader of Israel from Egypt, had predicted an end-time prophet like himself whom the people should heed (see Deut. 18:15). Elijah also was to prepare the way before the Messiah (see Mal. 3:1; 4:5, 6).

What would the presence of these two Old Testament figures have meant to Peter, James, and John? (Matt. 17:3, 4)

. . . .

. . . .

What do you think the bright, enveloping cloud and the voice from heaven (see Matt. 3:17) meant to the disciples during the transfiguration of Jesus? (Matt. 17:5, 6)

. . . .

. . . .

The prophecy said that Elijah's goal was to heal the broken relationships of Israel before the Messiah arrived. If he failed, judgment would follow (see Mal. 4:5, 6). What did Jesus' comments about John the Baptist suggest about the future? (Matt. 17:10–13)

. . . .

. . . .

What is the greatest display of the glory of the Lord you have ever witnessed? What lasting impression has it made on you?

. . . .

. . . .

The transfiguration of Jesus reinforced the accuracy of Peter's confession that Jesus was the Christ (Matt. 16:16). The next incident revealed how partial the disciples' spiritual vision still was. The disciples had become used to healing diseases and casting out demons in the name of Jesus (Matt. 10:1, 8). How did Jesus assess their inability to heal the epileptic boy? (Matt. 17:17, 20)

. . . .

. . . .

In what ways do you think prayer and fasting would have prepared the disciples to heal the epileptic boy? (Matt. 17:21)

. . . .

. . . .

Why do you think spiritual power depends on the present strength of our relationship with Christ rather than our skills and past experience?

. . . .

. . . .

Jesus' first prediction of His impending death and resurrection resulted in a rebuke from Peter (Matt. 16:21, 22). Why do you think His second prediction produced a response of sorrow? (Matt. 17:22, 23)

. . . .

. . . .

◆ CHILDLIKE FAITH ◆

(Matthew 17:24—18:14)

It had taken great faith for the disciples to declare that Jesus was the Messiah. He knew it would take monumental faith to accept that He had to die and would rise again from the dead. Consequently Jesus launched into a major teaching effort to clarify for His disciples the true nature of faith.

Every Jewish adult male paid an annual tax of two drachma to support the operation of the temple. As a rabbi without visible support, Jesus could claim exemption from the tax.[2] Jesus identified with His countrymen by regularly paying the tax. How did His story about the king's son being free from taxes apply to Him and the temple tax? (Matt. 17:25, 26)

. . . .

. . . .

Why do you think Jesus chose such an odd and supernatural way to pay His and Peter's temple tax? What lesson could Peter learn from this incident? (Matt. 17:27)

. . . .

. . . .

CONSIDER THIS

Read the *Word in Life™ Study Bible (WILSB)* feature "Jesus and Taxation" (Matt. 17:24–27). "If the Son of God paid a voluntary tax in order to avoid offending those who did not understand who He was, how much more should we, as God's children, bend over backwards at times to avoid offending those who do not understand our liberty?"

Circle the letter of the statement that you think best captures the spirit of Jesus' example set by paying the temple tax.

a. It is always the loving thing to abstain from any activity that another Christian objects to.

b. Love limits liberty except when the objecting brother or sister is a self-righteous hypocrite.

c. Love discerns when liberty will hinder the growth of a believer who does not understand it and modifies liberty accordingly.

d. Love only limits liberty when liberty would tempt the weaker brother or sister to sin.

e. Christians should always resist the efforts of more scrupulous believers to restrict their liberty in order to teach them freedom.

What was different about the disciples' idea of greatness in the kingdom and Jesus' idea of greatness? (Matt. 18:1–5)

. . . .

. . . .

What qualities of childhood do you think Jesus had in mind when He held up a child as the model of a citizen of the kingdom of heaven?

. . . .

. . . .

What are some common ways that children are offended by adults that illustrate ways Christians are offended by unbelievers?

. . . .

. . . .

CONSIDER THIS

Read the *WILSB* feature "Exaggerating to Make a Point" (Matt. 18:8, 9). Matthew 18:8, 9 is very similar to 5:29, 30. The earlier passage showed the dangers of lust. The present one deals with failures to act with childlike faith.

What repeated sin has frustrated you to the point of wanting to do something drastic about it? Why?

. . . .

. . . .

How can you deal ruthlessly and decisively with the sin you identified? Who should hold you accountable?

. . . .

. . . .

Why are we sometimes tempted to question or look down on Christians of deep but simple faith? (Matt. 18:11)

. . . .

. . . .

How do you think the angels intervene on behalf of believers of childlike faith? (Matt. 18:11)

. . . .

. . . .

The 100 sheep in Jesus' story all represent believers, as shown by the fact that the stray is "one of these little ones" (v. 14). Jesus earlier indicated the terrible fate of anyone who caused a little one to stumble (vv. 6, 7). How does the Father treat the little one who strays? (Matt. 18:12–14)

. . . .

. . . .

Circle the number that best represents the degree of childlikeness inherent to your faith.

1 2 3 4 5 6 7 8 9 10

SKEPTICALLY ADULT — CHANGEABLY ADOLESCENT — OCCASIONALLY CHILDLIKE — REGULARLY CHILDLIKE

◆ Faith to Handle Offenses ◆
(Matthew 18:15–35)

So far Jesus had illustrated the trusting nature of faith by means of a child. He had stressed how serious it is in the eyes of God for anyone to offend one of His little ones. Eventually Jesus abandoned the imagery of childhood to teach about the offenses that inevitably occur within the family of faith.

What did Jesus say to do at each of these stages when trying to reconcile with a brother or sister who offends you?

◆ By yourself (Matt. 18:15)

. . . .

. . . .

◆ With two or three witnesses (Matt. 18:16)

. . . .

. . . .

◆ Before the congregation (Matt. 18:17)

. . . .

. . . .

◆ When all fails (Matt. 18:17)

. . . .

. . . .

How does united action within the church achieve the purposes of God in ways that individual action cannot? (Matt. 18:18–20)

. . . .

. . . .

The rabbis came to teach that one should forgive someone who sinned against him up to three times for the same offense.[3] Peter probably felt very noble offering to forgive seven times (Matt. 18:21). What did Jesus mean when He said to forgive a brother seventy times seven times? (Matt. 18:22)

. . . .

. . . .

CONSIDER THIS

Read the *WILSB* feature "Seventy Times Seven—Still Not Enough!" (Matt. 18:21–35). "The first servant owed the king more than the second servant owed the first servant by a ratio of at least 600,000-to-1!"

In Jesus' story, why did the king forgive the servant with the massive debt? (Matt. 18:23–27)

. . . .

. . . .

In Jesus' story, why did the first servant refuse to forgive the other servant who owed him just a little? (Matt. 18:28–30)

. . . .

. . . .

Jesus taught His disciples to pray, "Forgive us our debts, as we forgive our debtors" (Matt. 6:12). How is the unforgiving servant in Jesus' story a negative illustration of this principle? (Matt. 18:31–34)

. . . .

. . . .

Circle the number that best represents your ability to forgive offenses against you.

1	2	3	4	5	6	7	8	9	10
WELL-NURSED GRUDGES		FITS OF FORGIVENESS				FORGIVENESS IS HARD WORK		LOVE TO FORGIVE	

What kind of offenses make you want to hold a grudge against the offender?

. . . .

. . . .

What aspects of the forgiveness God has granted you do you need to meditate on to motivate you to have a more forgiving spirit?

. . . .

. . . .

Faith to See Through Tricks

(Matthew 19:1–30)

Jesus left Galilee for the last time and headed for Judea where He faced betrayal and crucifixion (Matt. 19:1). The remainder of Matthew focuses on the teaching of Jesus in the interval before the end. First the Pharisees approached Jesus with a question about divorce—a knotty problem of the day (v. 3). They expected Him to antagonize a lot of people no matter what He said.

What did Jesus conclude about the nature of marriage from the creation account? (Matt. 19:4–6)

. . . .

. . . .

What did Jesus conclude about divorce from the Law of Moses? (Matt. 19:7–9)

. . . .

. . . .

Jesus' disciples were dismayed because Jesus interpreted the Old Testament to leave fewer options for remarriage than Jewish commentators

(Matt. 19:10).[4] What did Jesus have to say about reasons for celibacy? How widespread do you think He expected celibacy to be? (Matt. 19:11, 12)

. . . .

. . . .

CONSIDER THIS

Read the *WILSB* feature "The Challenge of Commitment" (Matt. 19:1–15). "Followers of Christ need to be known for their commitment—to marriage, to family, to community, to work, above all to Christ. Such loyalty often means messy obedience."

What do you think are the primary pressures working against commitments to the relationships of marriage, family, and friendships?

. . . .

. . . .

What are the fundamental theological concepts that call us to make and keep commitments to the primary people in our lives?

. . . .

. . . .

What relationship in your life would benefit most from more commitment on your part? Identify a practical step you can make to improve that commitment.

. . . .

. . . .

Jesus rebuked His disciples for trying to send away children brought to Him by their parents for a blessing (Matt. 19:13). What lessons that Jesus had been emphasizing repeatedly were the disciples overlooking? (Matt. 19:14, 15)

. . . .

. . . .

CONSIDER THIS

Read the *WILSB* feature "Children and Childcare" (Matt. 19:14). For "first-century women . . . their work and their homes were tightly linked, so they did not have to surmount the challenges of specialization and separation."

In a culture that fragments families, what can churches do to help families pull together and grow strong?

. . . .

. . . .

How can mothers and fathers maintain intimacy with their children when work requires them to use childcare services?

. . . .

. . . .

What do you think the rich young man really wanted to hear from Jesus? (Matt. 19:16, 20)

. . . .

. . . .

Why do you think Jesus asked the rich young man to sell everything and distribute his wealth to the poor? (Matt. 19:21, 22)

. . . .

. . . .

Why is it harder for a rich man to be saved than for a camel to go through the eye of a needle? What hope of salvation do wealthy people have? (Matt. 19:23–26)

. . . .

. . . .

What reward awaited Jesus' disciples for the sacrifices they had made for the kingdom of heaven? (Matt. 19:27, 28)

. . . .

. . . .

What rewards await Christians who have made sacrifices for the kingdom of heaven? (Matt. 19:29, 30)

. . . .

. . . .

How has the Lord already blessed you within your community of believers?

. . . .

. . . .

1. C. S. Lewis, *The Lion, the Witch and the Wardrobe* (New Y ork: Macmillan Publishing Co., Inc., 1950).

2. Craig S. Keener, 92.

3. *Ibid.*, 95.

4. D. A. Carson, 411.

LESSON 9

Who Said Faith Is Easy?

Matthew 20:1—21:46

When Peter, Susan, Edmund, and Lucy entered Narnia in The Lion, the Witch and the Wardrobe, *none of the children had any idea that they would become part of a great conflict between forces of good and evil. Soon they began to hear of Aslan the lion and the White Witch who was queen of Narnia.*

A family of beavers claimed that Aslan was the rightful ruler of Narnia and that the White Witch was a wicked usurper. Edmund, however, had met the White Witch and found her charming. He wondered if she might be the rightful ruler and Aslan a vicious beast.

The children faced several hindrances to faith in Aslan as the savior of Narnia. Susan and Lucy were very uneasy that he was a dangerous beast —a lion, no less. Peter wondered why he should fulfill the ancient prophecies rather than the White Witch. Lucy worried that she had caused harm to others by getting involved in Narnia. Edmund knew that following Aslan would cost him the rewards promised him by the White Witch.

There were plenty of hindrances to faith during the lifetime of Jesus. The disciples of Jesus struggled to understand and trust their Master. The masses of ordinary people had a hard time deciding how the tender Messiah fit into their expectations. The Jewish leaders thought Jesus was dangerously revolutionary.

◆ The Long and Short of Faith ◆

(Matthew 20:1–16)

Years after Jesus died, the apostle Paul wrote to the Ephesian church, "For by grace you have been saved through faith, and that not of yourselves; it is the gift of God" (Eph. 2:8). Jesus' parable of the workmen's wages illustrated how my faith can be hindered by a sense that I deserve God's grace more than you do.

The work day in Jesus' time was roughly 6:00 A.M. until 6:00 P.M. Those hours were numbered one through twelve. About ten hours were devoted to labor and the rest to meals and breaks.[1] Complete the following chart about the five groups of laborers in Jesus' parable hired by the landowner to work in his vineyard.

GROUP NUMBER	TIME HIRED	AGREED WAGES	HOURS WORKED
1 (Matt. 20:2)			
2 (Matt. 20:3, 4)			
3 (Matt. 20:5)			
4 (Matt. 20:5)			
5 (Matt. 20:6, 7)			

Why did the original laborers assume they would receive more pay than they had contracted for? (Matt. 20:8–10)

How did the landowner explain why he paid the same wage for the varying amounts of work performed by the different groups? (Matt. 20:11–15)

In what ways do pride about length of service and devotion to the Lord hinder the kind of faith Jesus wants to nurture in His disciples?

CONSIDER THIS

Read the *Word in Life™ Study Bible (WILSB)* feature "Jesus and Unjust Pay" (Matt. 20:1–16). "Jesus was not encouraging unjust pay scales and discrimination. He was merely illustrating the nature of God's grace in terms that His followers could understand."

If an employer actually paid his workers the way the landowner did in Jesus' parable, what would happen to his workforce?

Does Jesus' parable encourage "deathbed conversions" as a way of cashing in on the grace of God? Why or why not?

◆ WEAK FAITH IS BLIND ◆

(Matthew 20:17–34)

Faith is frequently hindered by our inability to perceive spiritual realities. All through His earthly ministry to His disciples, Jesus struggled against His disciples' false conceptions of who He was and what He had come to do. They also had all sorts of erroneous notions about their role in the kingdom of heaven.

What did Jesus tell His disciples in this third prediction of His impending death (Matt. 20:17–19) that He had not revealed in the first two (16:21 and 17:22, 23)?

. . . .

. . . .

What kind of response(s) do you think Jesus wanted His disciples to have to His prediction? (Matt. 20:17–19)

. . . .

. . . .

What was wrong with the response they made? (Matt. 20:20–28)

. . . .

. . . .

CONSIDER THIS

Read the *WILSB* feature "A Pushy Mother" (Matt. 20:20–23). "But how often are we like [James and John]—eager to promise whatever we have to in order to get what we want?"

Why do honor and prestige naturally appeal to us more than suffering and servanthood?

. . . .

. . . .

Why are suffering and servanthood fundamental to all spiritual honor in the kingdom of heaven?

. . . .

. . . .

Why should we always let the Lord designate who will be honored in His kingdom?

. . . .

. . . .

CONSIDER THIS

Read the *WILSB* feature "Servant-Leaders" (Matt. 20:25–28). "Responding to a controversy among the disciples (vv. 25–28), Jesus revealed a unique style of authority—servant leadership."

What are some typical ways that people in the world measure authority?

. . . .

. . . .

How do you think servanthood establishes spiritual authority among the followers of Jesus? (Matt. 20:26–28)

. . . .

. . . .

As Jesus approached Jerusalem and corrected His disciples' spiritual blindness, what new dimensions of His own impending suffering did He show them? (Matt. 20:28)

. . . .

. . . .

If Christ had not ransomed you, to what spiritual blindness and sin do you think you would be enslaved?

. . . .

. . . .

Jesus left Jericho in the presence of His disciples and a multitude of other Galilean pilgrims bound for Jerusalem to observe the Passover (Matt. 20:29). How did the two blind men by the roadside demonstrate spiritual insight? (Matt. 20:29, 30, 32)

. . . .

. . . .

How did the people with Jesus demonstrate spiritual blindness in their response to the physically blind men? (Matt. 20:31)

. . . .

. . . .

Which do you think is easier for Jesus to heal: physical or spiritual blindness? Why?

. . . .

. . . .

Describe an incident of sudden spiritual insight that came as though the Lord had touched the eyes of your soul.

. . . .

. . . .

◆ BLESSED BELIEVERS; CURSED UNBELIEVERS ◆

(Matthew 21:1–22)

Some of those who hesitated about whether to respond to Jesus were hindered by the exuberant faith of those who welcomed Him into Jerusalem on the Sunday before Passover. At least they said they were (Matt. 21:15). Perhaps it was their power and position that hindered them from letting go of their somber decorum and joining in shouting hosannas to the King.

How did Jesus show both humility and authority in arranging to enter Jerusalem? (Matt. 21:1–3)

◆ Humility

. . . .

. . . .

◆ Authority

. . . .

. . . .

Who do you know who combines humility and authority in the way they conduct themselves? What characteristics of that person do you want to be true of you?

. . . .

. . . .

CONSIDER THIS

Read the *WILSB* feature "A New Style of Fame" (Matt. 21:8–11). "But instead of a parade of chariots and trumpets and a well-orchestrated ceremony, Jesus chose to ride into town on a donkey, a common beast of burden; no prancing warhorse for Him!"

What did the composite prophecy from Zechariah and Isaiah reveal about Jesus? (Matt. 21:5)

. . . .

. . . .

Hosanna originally meant "Save us!" but had become an exclamation of praise in Jewish worship. As the multitude chanted Psalm 118:25, 26, what were they confessing about Jesus? (Matt. 21:9)

. . . .

. . . .

What did the exchange between the residents of Jerusalem and the parading pilgrim show about their understanding of who Jesus was? (Matt. 21:10, 11)

. . . .

. . . .

Pilgrims needed to buy animals for sacrifices. Temple taxes needed to be made in local coinage rather than the currency of other regions or nations. The money-changing and animal-selling were carefully segregated from the worship areas of the sprawling temple complex. What do you think Jesus was really objecting to that perverted the temple's function as a place of worship? (Matt. 21:12, 13)

. . . .

. . . .

Jesus objected to commerce in the temple (Matt. 21:12, 13); the chief priests and scribes objected to Jesus healing and accepting praise in the temple (vv. 14, 15). Why didn't the leaders want those things happening there?

. . . .

. . . .

How did the children show more insight and faith than the religious experts and authorities? (Matt. 21:15, 16)

. . . .

. . . .

Leaves and the earliest bitter-tasting green fruit appeared on Palestinian fig trees at the same time.[2] Sometimes the green figs fell from the tree leaving just the leaves. How did the leafy fig tree without fruit picture the faith of some of the people around Jesus in Jerusalem? Whom may He have had in mind? (Matt. 21:18, 19)

. . . .

. . . .

The disciples missed the point of the curse on the fig tree in their excitement about the miracle (Matt. 21:20). What do you think Jesus promised when He said faith and prayer could cast mountains into the sea? (Matt. 21:21, 22)

. . . .

. . . .

◆ DELIBERATE FAITHFULNESS ◆

(Matthew 21:23–46)

Finally the Jewish religious authorities abandoned any pretense of civility with Jesus. Their own choice effectively hindered any faith they could have had in Him. Jesus boldly and clearly exposed the calculated nature of their unbelief. Nobody—neither onlookers nor the religious leaders—missed the point of who Jesus was talking about. It was their last chance to repent.

CONSIDER THIS

Read the *WILSB* feature "A Challenge to Authority" (Matt. 21:23–27). "Jesus faced a direct challenge to His authority from the chief priests and elders, the top leadership in Israel (vv. 23–27). In this instance He didn't argue with them, but simply tossed the ball back into their court."

Why do you think Jesus refused to answer directly the questions of the leaders about His authority to cleanse the temple? (Matt. 21:23)

. . . .

. . . .

What did Jesus reveal about the chief priests and elders by asking them about the authority of John the Baptist? (Matt. 21:24–27)

. . . .

. . . .

CONSIDER THIS

Read the *WILSB* feature "Is Evasion Ethical?" (Matt. 21:24–27). "Rather than being unethically evasive, Jesus was merely diverting an evil plot in a discrete manner by posing a difficult question. A simple yes or no answer would have played right into their hands."

Do you think the chief priests and scribes felt as though Jesus had evaded them or exposed them? (Matt. 21:24–27) Why do you think this way?

. . . .

. . . .

What are some kinds of questions or challenges that you think might better be deflected than answered directly?

. . . .

. . . .

How had the tax collectors and harlots behaved like the first son in Jesus' story? (Matt. 21:28, 29, 31, 32)

. . . .

. . . .

How had the chief priests and elders behaved like the second son in Jesus' story? (Matt. 21:30, 31, 32)

. . . .

. . . .

Describe an incident in which you behaved like the first son and another incident in which you acted like the second son.

◆ First son

. . . .

. . . .

◆ Second son

. . . .

. . . .

CONSIDER THIS

Read the *WILSB* feature "`Harlots Enter the Kingdom'" (Matt. 21:31, 32). "Faith was the key to the kingdom; yet even prostitutes were showing more faith in Christ than those who were viewed as `righteous.'"

Who are regarded as the most disreputable kinds of people in your community?

. . . .

. . . .

What are the greatest hindrances to reaching these people with the gospel of Christ?

. . . .

. . . .

How do you think Jesus would have reached out to them? What can your church do along these same lines?

. . . .

. . . .

The parable of the vineyard owner is similar to an allegory in which each element of the story represents something or someone. Who or what does each part of this parable represent? (Matt. 21:33–39)

◆ The landowner

. . . .

. . . .

◆ The vineyard

. . . .

. . . .

◆ The vinedressers

. . . .

. . . .

◆ The servants

. . . .

. . . .

◆ The son

. . . .

. . . .

Why did Jesus ask the chief priests and Pharisees to finish the story rather than drawing the conclusion for them? (Matt. 21:40, 41)

. . . .

. . . .

1. D. A. Carson, 427.
2. Craig S. Keener, 102.

LESSON 10

Unbelief: Playing with Fire

Matthew 22:1—23:39

Four children entered Narnia in C. S. Lewis' The Lion, the Witch and the Wardrobe. *An ancient Narnian prophecy stated that two sons of Adam and two daughters of Eve would bring in a golden age under the direction of the great lion Aslan. Unbeknownst to the other three, Edmund had met the White Witch who illegitimately ruled Narnia and kept it in perpetual winter and had sworn allegiance to her.*

When the children began to hear about Aslan from Mr. and Mrs. Beaver, Edmund could not believe what they said. The White Witch had promised him power and position. He wanted to get even for imagined offenses by his older brother Peter. When no one was looking, Edmund slipped away from the others to betray them to the White Witch.

Edmund's unbelief blinded him to the truth about Aslan and the witch. He had truth and falsehood confused. He had to deny the Narnian sacred writings because they did not serve his ends. Before much time elapsed in the story, Edmund's life was in jeopardy, his brother and sisters were at risk, and he hated himself for being such a fool. Finally, it looked as though his unbelief would lead to the death of Aslan and the total victory of the White Witch.

Unbelief is dangerous. In The Lion, the Witch and the Wardrobe, *Edmund's selfish rebellion threatened the whole land of Narnia. In the Gospel of Matthew, the settled unbelief of the Jewish leaders put the whole nation at risk. They faced stern judgment for their role in rejecting the Son of God.*

Unbelief Offends God

(Matthew 22:1–14)

When someone hears the gospel of Christ repeatedly, thinks seriously about it, and rejects it, that person's unbelief is not a casual thing. No longer can he or she claim ignorance or disinterest. That person has entered the ranks of active unbelievers. As with the religious authorities of Jesus' day, the worst danger of active unbelief is becoming an enemy of God.

The parable of the vinedressers (Matt. 21:33–41) focused on the rebelliousness of the tenant farmers. The next parable Jesus told the chief priests and Pharisees highlighted the consequences of such arrogance. How did the noblemen in the story offend their king? (Matt. 22:2–7)

. . . .

. . . .

What were the consequences of their behavior? (Matt. 22:7)

. . . .

. . . .

CONSIDER THIS

Read the *Word in Life™ Study Bible (WILSB)* feature "Worse Than Rude" (Matt. 22:2–14). "God had sent Israel an early `invitation' to His Son's wedding through the Old Testament Law and prophets. Now that Jesus had arrived, proclaiming the second invitation, the nation was rejecting Him—a perilous choice."

Palestinian wedding celebrations lasted about a week, so guests needed advance notice to arrange for such a lengthy absence from their livelihoods. The second announcement launched the festivities. What did the noblemen communicate to their king by their reaction to both announcements? (Matt. 22:2–6)

. . . .

. . . .

How do people today continue to repeat the rebellion of the chief priests and Pharisees?

. . . .

. . . .

How did the king fill his son's wedding banquet after the invited guests scorned the privilege offered them? (Matt. 22:8–10)

. . . .

. . . .

How does this parallel the way God has populated the kingdom of heaven?

. . . .

. . . .

One of the poor guests was punished severely for coming to the wedding feast in his everyday clothes (Matt. 22:11–13). What do you think this represents in terms of how people respond to the gospel of Christ?

. . . .

. . . .

Both active hostility (Matt. 22:2–7) and casual indifference (vv. 11–13) to the kingdom of heaven result in severe punishment. Identify a friend or acquaintance who has no interest in Christ.

. . . .

. . . .

On the following scale, circle the number that best represents that person's attitude toward the gospel.

1 2 3 4 5 6 7 8 9 10

HOSTILITY CONFUSION INDIFFERENCE

How do you think you should pray for this friend or acquaintance you described above?

. . . .

. . . .

Unbelief Trifles with Truth
(Matthew 22:15–45)

The increasingly frustrated opponents of Jesus launched a series of attempts to discredit Him. They posed a variety of tests and challenges to Him that Jesus handled skillfully. The questioners were disappointed because they weren't interested in the truth. They wanted Him to make a fool of Himself.

Why do you think the Pharisees and Herodians flattered Jesus before posing their trick question? (Matt. 22:16)

. . . .

. . . .

Circle the letter of the following statement that best represents how you respond when someone flatters you.

a. My ego swells with pride, and I am susceptible to anything the flatterer wants of me.

b. I admire the flatterer's perception of my good qualities but listen objectively to anything else presented.

c. I stop the flattery and ask the speaker to start again without irrelevant personal references.

d. Experience has taught me to screen out flattery so I can focus on the substantive part of our communication.

e. A warning signal goes off in my head, and I distrust everything else the flatterer says.

The Pharisees regarded God as sovereign among the Jews and disliked paying Roman taxes. The Herodians collaborated with Rome and regarded Roman taxes as reasonable. Most ordinary people agreed with the anti-tax sentiment of the Pharisees. How did Jesus' answer to their question address the basic concern of both groups?

. . . .

. . . .

What church-state issue(s) might a critic of Christianity raise to try to trip up a spiritual leader today?

. . . .

. . . .

How does the principle Jesus stated apply to the issue(s) you identified above?

. . . .

. . . .

Why did the Sadducees consider their scenario of one woman with seven successive husbands a serious critique of the idea of resurrection from the dead? (Matt. 22:23–28)

. . . .

. . . .

The Sadducees regarded only the first five books of the Old Testament—written by Moses—as the Word of God. So Jesus quoted Exodus 3:6 for them (Matt. 22:32). How did Jesus show their ignorance of the Scripture and the power of God? (Matt. 22:29–32)

◆ The Scripture

. . . .

. . . .

◆ The power of God

. . . .

. . . .

CONSIDER THIS

Read the *WILSB* feature "Trick Questions Foiled" (Matt. 22:23–33). "Are you known as a speaker of truth among your peers? Are there ways you could be more forthright and helpful in your communications?"

How do you think the Sadducees thought their trick question would make Jesus look bad? (Matt. 22:23–28)

. . . .

. . . .

What sinful attitudes usually are at work when someone tries to humiliate another in public?

. . . .

. . . .

What practices should you avoid to ensure that you are "forthright and helpful" in your conversations with others?

. . . .

. . . .

Pharisaic debates about the relative importance of Old Testament laws (Matt. 22:34) were common in Jesus' day.[1] The Pharisees probably wanted to draw Jesus into any possible controversy to drag him down to the level of ordinary petty squabbling. Why was Jesus' response virtually impossible for the Pharisees to argue with? (Matt. 22:37–39)

. . . .

. . . .

What do you think Jesus meant when He said "all the Law and Prophets" hang from these two commandments? (Matt. 22:40)

. . . .

. . . .

CONSIDER THIS

Read the *WILSB* feature "What Kind of Love Is This?" (Matt. 22:34–40). "God wants to deliver a new kind of love—agapē love—to families, workplaces, and communities through His people."

How do you think love of God is foundational to love of other people?

. . . .

. . . .

Who around you needs to experience the love of a Christian friend? How can you help meet that need?

. . . .

. . . .

After the Jewish leaders had tried repeatedly to stump Jesus, He directed some questions at them. They could identify the Messiah as the Son of David (Matt. 22:42), but they had no idea what to say about David calling the Messiah Lord (vv. 43–45). What had David prophetically recognized about the Messiah that the Pharisees of Jesus' day did not?

. . . .

. . . .

◆ Unbelief is Proud ◆

(Matthew 23:1–12)

If faith in Christ leads to genuine humility, it stands to reason that unbelief will lead to pride in its worst degrees. The series of eight woes (Matt. 23:13, 14, 15, 16, 23, 25, 27, 29) Jesus pronounced against the prideful scribes and Pharisees read like a revolutionary antithesis to the Beatitudes the tender Messiah prescribed for His humble disciples (5:3–10).

What authority did the scribes and Pharisees have, and how had they abused it? (Matt. 23:1–7)

. . . .

. . . .

How did Jesus describe the authority He wants to see exercised among His disciples?

◆ Negatively (Matt. 23:8–10)

. . . .

. . . .

◆ Positively (Matt. 23:11, 12)

. . . .

. . . .

What temptations to proud attitudes and behaviors do you have to resist when you serve as a leader?

. . . .

. . . .

◆ Unbelief is Hypocritical ◆

(Matthew 23:13–28)

Unbelief is dangerous because it denies certain spiritual realities. Unbelief has to make up ideas and practices to take the place of the reality it denies. Consequently unbelief has to be hypocritical at every point it pretends to know how to think and act when it really doesn't. This made Jesus furious at the scribes and Pharisees.

For each of the first seven woes Jesus pronounced upon the scribes and Pharisees, summarize the charge against them and state how it revealed their hypocrisy.

The First Woe (Matt. 23:13)

◆ The charge

. . . .

. . . .

◆ The hypocrisy

. . . .

. . . .

The Second Woe (Matt. 23:14)

◆ The charge

. . . .

. . . .

◆ The hypocrisy

. . . .

. . . .

The Third Woe (Matt. 23:15)

◆ The charge

. . . .

. . . .

◆ The hypocrisy

The Fourth Woe (Matt. 23:16–22)

◆ The charge

◆ The hypocrisy

The Fifth Woe (Matt. 23:23, 24)

◆ The charge

◆ The hypocrisy

The Sixth Woe (Matt. 23:25, 26)

◆ The charge

◆ The hypocrisy

The Seventh Woe (Matt. 23:27, 28)

◆ The charge

◆ The hypocrisy

CONSIDER THIS

Read the *WILSB* feature "Growing Fat at the Poor's Expense" (Matt. 23:14). Jesus' "stiff rebuke of the Pharisees challenges any of us involved in finance and deal-making to carefully weigh the ethics of our choices. Woe to us if we devour the resources of the disadvantaged."

In your work, your consumption of goods and resources, your voting patterns, and your political views, how can you keep in mind the needs of the poor and oppressed?

. . . .

. . . .

◆ Unbelief is Violent ◆

(Matthew 23:29–39)

The scribes and Pharisees thought they were better than their ancestors who had mistreated the Old Testament prophets. Jesus claimed that their unbelief made them as violence-prone as their faithless forefathers. Nothing has changed. Unbelief still thinks it is progressive and humane, while it condones violent hatred.

Why did the scribes and Pharisees think they were less dangerous than their faithless ancestors? (Matt. 23:20–30)

. . . .

. . . .

Jesus claimed the scribes and Pharisees would carry to completion the violence of their ancestors (Matt. 23:31–33). What did He predict they would do? (Matt. 23:34–36)

. . . .

. . . .

According to your reading or other sources, where in the world are Christians suffering atrocities at the hands of unbelievers? What is happening there?

. . . .

. . . .

1. D. A. Carson, 464.

LESSON 11

Faith Penetrates the Future

Matthew 24:1—25:46

C. S. Lewis wrote The Lion, the Witch and the Wardrobe *in 1950. In quick succession he wrote a book a year for the next six years, completing* The Chronicles of Narnia *in 1956 with the publication of* The Last Battle. *Fans of these children's stories have their favorites, but* The Last Battle *seldom rates at the top of the list.*

What's wrong with *The Last Battle*? It has a tight plot, a cast of intriguing characters, and rip-roaring action. If anything the suspense is too high for young children. In addition, *The Last Battle* gives us such unforgettable Lewisisms as "Shadowlands," the title for the award-winning motion pictures about Lewis and Joy Davidman, and "Further up and further in," a call to enjoy the presence of God.

The Last Battle is a difficult story to enjoy because the good guys lose in the normal sense of the word. It's the end of the world for Narnia, and no matter what the Narnian heroes do with the help of the visiting children, they are frustrated at the last moment by the villains. The victory—and it's a grand one—happens in the Narnian heaven after the last battle.

It's a sobering story about grit and determination in the face of overwhelming odds. When the tender Messiah sat with His disciples on the Mount of Olives and looked down on the temple complex, He told them an equally grim tale about the revolutionary faith they needed for a difficult future—a future filled with conflict that would end with victory in the kingdom of heaven after a great judgment.

Trouble Precedes Triumph

(Matthew 24:1–35)

After Jesus had pronounced His series of woes on the scribes and Pharisees (Matt. 23:13–30) and predicted the desolation of the temple (v. 38), He led His disciples out of Jerusalem and headed up the Mount of Olives to return to Bethany (24:1). As He talked with His disciples about the temple spread out below them, Jesus elaborated on its impending destruction (v. 2). What two questions did the disciples ask of Jesus? (Matt. 24:3)

◆ 1.

. . . .

. . . .

◆ 2.

. . . .

. . . .

What spiritual danger did Jesus warn His disciples to avoid while they wait for his return? (Matt. 24:4, 5)

. . . .

. . . .

What ongoing sorrows that will characterize the time until Jesus returns make people vulnerable to deception by false Christs? (Matt. 24:6–8)

. . . .

. . . .

What other spiritual threats during the time before Jesus returns did He warn could harm the faith of His disciples? (Matt. 24:9–12)

. . . .

. . . .

◆ (vv. 9, 10)

. . . .

. . . .

◆ (v. 11)

. . . .

. . . .

◆ (v. 12)

. . . .

. . . .

What good news did Jesus offer His disciples about the coming difficult days? (Matt. 24:13, 14)

. . . .

. . . .

In addition to the general spiritual dangers of the future, Jesus detailed the destruction of Jerusalem and the temple (which occurred at the hands of Roman armies between A.D. 66 and 70). In A.D. 66, Jewish Zealots assassinated several priests in the temple. In A.D. 70 the Roman conquerors brought the Roman standard, which ascribed divinity to the emperor, into the temple area. Both events were unimaginable acts of desecration that may be the "'abomination of desolation' spoken of by Daniel the prophet" (Matt. 24:15).[1]

How did Jesus advise His disciples to respond when the arrival of "the abomination of desolation" indicated that Jerusalem was about to be destroyed? (Matt. 24:16–20)

. . . .

. . . .

There is pretty good traditional evidence that the Christians of Jerusalem left in A.D. 68 and hid in the Judean hills northeast of the city.[2] How did Jesus characterize the intensity of the Roman siege and annihilation of Jerusalem? (Matt. 24:21, 22)

. . . .

. . . .

The disciples had asked about the signs of Jesus' second coming (Matt. 24:3). He had indicated that there would be many false Christs (v. 5). How will the false Christs present themselves? (Matt. 24:23–25)

. . . .

. . . .

What will be different about the arrival of the false Christs and the return of the true Christ? (Matt. 24:26–28)

. . . .

. . . .

What will be the events associated with the second coming of Christ? (Matt. 24:29–31)

◆ (v. 29)

. . . .

. . . .

◆ (v. 30)

. . . .

. . . .

◆ (v. 31)

. . . .

. . . .

In Matthew 24:33, "these things" refer to all of the signs preceding the return of Christ and "it" refers to His return. Assuming "these things" has the same meaning in v. 34, what did Jesus predict would happen in the lifetime of the group He spoke to that day? (Matt. 24:34)

. . . .

. . . .

What kinds of people do you think are most vulnerable to the claims of phony messiahs?

. . . .

. . . .

What forms of persecution would you most dread facing for the name of Christ?

. . . .

. . . .

What comfort can you draw from the promise of the Lord to shorten persecution for the sake of His chosen ones? (Matt. 24:22)

. . . .

. . . .

◆ THE WATCHFUL TRIUMPH ◆

(Matthew 24:36–51)

The first part of Jesus' address to His disciples answered their questions about the destruction of Jerusalem and the Lord's return at the end of the age (Matt. 24:3). The rest of chapter 24 and all of chapter 25 discuss how to live by faith during the interval between the present and His return. The first quality Jesus advocated was watchfulness or anticipation.

What did Jesus have to say about the exact timing of His return? (Matt, 24:36)

. . . .

. . . .

Circle the letter(s) of the statement(s) that best expresses why in your opinion people through the centuries have tried to set dates for the Second Coming of Jesus.

a. Many people have a longing to know secrets that no one else knows. Secret knowledge makes them feel superior to ordinary Christians.

b. Some prophecy teachers get carried away with their own dogmatism about the last days until they believe they have found interpretive answers about the last days that no one else has.

c. Date-setting has the occult quality of giving people control over the future. If you know when something is going to happen, you can arrange things to your advantage.

d. Date-setting is tabloid theology. Some people want everything exciting and titillating, so some popular speakers and writers give it to them.

e. The devil likes to agitate the body of Christ, so he tries to distort the truth. Setting dates for the Second Coming is one way of doing this.

In what ways were the days of Noah like the future time when Jesus will return? (Matt. 24:37, 39)

. . . .

. . . .

What do the brief stories of two men in the field and two women grinding teach about anticipating the coming of the Son of Man? (Matt. 24:40, 41)

. . . .

. . . .

In what ways will the return of Christ be like a thief robbing a house? (Matt. 24:42–44)

. . . .

. . . .

Jesus compared watchful and selfish disciples to the faithful and faithless servants of an absentee master (Matt. 24:45–51). What does each of these elements of the story teach about watching for the return of Christ?

◆ The faithful and wise servant (vv. 45–47)

. . . .

. . . .

◆ The evil servant (vv. 48, 49)

. . . .

. . . .

◆ The severe punishment of the evil servant (vv. 50, 51)

. . . .

. . . .

Circle the number on the following scale that rates how well you think you watch for the return of Christ.

1	2	3	4	5	6	7	8	9	10
NEVER THINK ABOUT IT		GLANCE UP OCCASIONALLY				AN EYE ON THE SKY		BOTH EYES LOOKING UP	

◆ The Prepared Triumph ◆

(Matthew 25:1–13)

Jesus wants more from His followers than anticipation that He might return at any time. He also wants us to be prepared when He comes. That preparation may consist of different things for different disciples.

An Oriental wedding celebration began when the bridegroom and his party came at nightfall to the bride's home. Friends of the bride were expected to go out and escort the groom and his friends the last portion of the way. In Jesus' wedding story, what distinguished the wise virgins from the foolish ones? (Matt. 25:1–4)

. . . .

. . . .

It's likely that the lamps of the virgins had burned while they slept until the oil in them was gone. When then did the foolish virgins realize they weren't prepared to meet the bridegroom? (Matt. 25:6, 7)

. . . .

. . . .

Why couldn't the wise virgins share their supply of oil with the foolish ones? (Matt. 25:8, 9)

. . . .

. . . .

Circle the letter of the statement that best explains the meaning of the foolish virgins' exclusion from the wedding celebration. (Matt. 25:10–12)

a. You can't repent at the last moment. You have to do good long enough to satisfy God.

b. Moral purity isn't enough to gain entrance into heaven. You have to do good works.

c. Foolish people can't be Christians.

d. The absence of oil showed that they did not have the Holy Spirit and were not true believers.

e. Their lack of preparation revealed the faithlessness of their hearts.

Circle the letter of the statement that best explains the meaning of the wise virgins' preparation for the arrival of the bridegroom. (Matt. 25:10)

a. Their supply of oil indicated that they were filled with the Holy Spirit and prepared for the Second Coming.

b. They had lived their lives prior to the bridegroom's arrival in such a way that their faith had prepared them to be with Him at any time.

c. Not only were they morally pure, but they had fortified themselves with many good works.

d. They had repented of their sins long before the last moment and pleased God with many righteous deeds.

e. They were wise enough to be good Christians.

Circle the number on the following scale that rates how well you think you are prepared for the return of Christ.

1	2	3	4	5	6	7	8	9	10
PLEASE, NOT NOW			I'M TRYING			NOT TOO BAD		PLEASE, COME NOW	

THE DILIGENT TRIUMPH
(Matthew 25:14–30)

Watchfulness is the faithful attitude that demonstrates the heart is right. Preparation is the faithful pattern that proves the life is right. Diligence, the third quality of future-faith, is the commitment that reveals the will is right.

In the parable of the talents, why did the businessman give different amounts of money into the care of his three managers? (Matt. 25:14, 15)

. . . .

. . . .

What did the managers understand they were to do with their master's money? (Matt. 25:16–18, 24)

. . . .

. . . .

When the businessman returned, how did he respond to the diligence of the first two managers? (Matt. 25:20–23)

. . . .

. . . .

How was the third manager's immobilizing fear a result of lack of faith in his master? (Matt. 25:24, 25)

. . . .

. . . .

How do you think each of the following misconceptions about the character of Jesus would affect a person's ability to be diligent in serving Him?

◆ He isn't interested in me as an individual

. . . .

. . . .

◆ He can't wait to punish me each time I sin

. . . .

. . . .

◆ He's my best buddy no matter how I act or think

. . . .

. . . .

◆ He wants me handing out tracts and preaching on street corners twenty-four hours a day

. . . .

. . . .

◆ He should be glad someone like me believed in Him

. . . .

. . . .

Jesus used the third manager to illustrate how diligence can demonstrate whether a professing disciple really has faith in the Lord. What do you think is the connection between genuine faith and diligent service? (Matt. 25:26–30)

. . . .

. . . .

Circle the number on the following scale that rates how diligent you think you are as you wait for the return of Christ.

1	2	3	4	5	6	7	8	9	10
SHIFTLESS SKUNK			FLIGHTY BIRD			PLODDING PONY		BUSY BEE	

CONSIDER THIS

Read the *Word in Life Study Bible (WILSB)* feature "True Success Means Faithfulness" (Matt. 25:14–30). "God measures our success not by what we have, but by what we do with what we have—for all that we have is a gift from Him."

What would you call your greatest "success" in life in terms of faithfulness to God as the giver of all you have? Why do you rate this so highly?

. . . .

. . . .

The Compassionate Triumph

(Matthew 25:31–46)

Jesus taught one more thing about future-oriented faith. By itself, diligence can be a hardheaded, hard-hearted characteristic. The final message teaches that diligence must be paired with compassion among the attitudes of a faithful follower of the coming King.

How do the setting and function of the returning Son of man show that Jesus equated Himself in deity with His Father? (Matt. 25:31–34)

. . . .

. . . .

Jesus anticipates many disciples from around the world. On what basis will the Judge recognize the faith of the "sheep"? (Matt. 25:32–36)

. . . .

. . . .

CONSIDER THIS

Read the *WILSB* feature "The Final Exam" (Matt. 25:31–46).

EXAM FOR THE NATIONS		
Were you a friend of Jesus when He was *hungry*?	yes	no
Were you a friend of Jesus when He was *thirsty*?	yes	no
Were you a friend of Jesus when He was *a stranger*?	yes	no
Were you a friend of Jesus when He was *naked*?	yes	no
Were you a friend of Jesus when He was *sick*?	yes	no
Were you a friend of Jesus when He was in *prison*?	yes	no

Why will the "sheep" be surprised by the King's assertion that they have done all of these acts of compassion to Him? (Matt. 25:37–39)

. . . .

. . . .

Why will the "goats" be startled to hear the King say they have mistreated Him when He was in need? (Matt. 25:44)

. . . .

. . . .

When did the "sheep" show compassion to the King and the "goats" withhold compassion from Him? (Matt. 25:40, 45)

. . . .

. . . .

Circle the number on the following scale that rates your compassion as you wait for the return of the Son of man.

1	2	3	4	5	6	7	8	9	10
ALL GOAT			GOATISH			SHEEPISH		ALL SHEEP	

1. Craig S. Keener, 112, 113.
2. D. A. Carson, 501.

The Tender King's Revolutionary Death, Resurrection, and Mission

Matthew 26:1—28:20

Matthew went out of his way to show how the early events of Jesus' life fulfilled the Old Testament Scripture (Matt. 1—4). In the same way he stressed the fulfillment aspects of the death, burial, and resurrection of Jesus. These closing chapters are filled with Old Testament quotations.

Matthew continued his emphasis on the mission of Jesus' disciples. The Great Commission is the fitting climax to this Gospel that records the inauguration of the reign of Christ in and through the lives of those who receive the kingdom of heaven. We must help others rejoice in the revolutionary message of the tender Messiah.

LESSON 12

The Abandoned King

Matthew 26:1—27:10

In The Gulag Archipelago, *Aleksandr Solzhenitsyn described a dizzying array of arrest procedures carried out by the secret police of the former Soviet Union. Nighttime and daytime arrests; at home, at work, and traveling arrests; first-time and repeat arrests; single and multiple arrests; surprise arrests; arrests with expected resistance; and arrests with searches.*[1]

Most arrests were sudden, but some were gradual. A Soviet citizen realized that all around him friends were being arrested. He stopped meeting and talking with anyone. Paranoia blossomed because any street vendor, bus driver, fellow pedestrian, meter reader, or sales clerk could be a secret policeman maneuvering him into a very private or very public place for a sudden arrest.

Then one day the local Communist Party committee summons him and gives him a commendation for his work and two passes to a Party vacation spot. He relaxes for the first time in weeks, packs with his wife, and goes to the rail station. There a young man strikes up a conversation and draws him aside for a moment. He disappears for ten years. "The station is thronged, and no one notices anything."[2]

These gradual arrests depended on the isolation of the suspicious victim from all of his safeguards and anyone who might protest. If the authorities were lucky, everyone would think the man skipped out on his wife until it was too late to look for him.

As the time of Jesus' death drew near, He too experienced isolation. He was isolated from friends who did not understand His mission. He was isolated from authorities who plotted His death. Finally He was cornered in a lonely garden and arrested by desperate authorities who hoped to railroad His execution before His supporters realized what was happening.

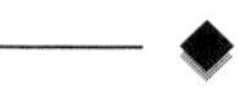

Alone As a Target

(Matthew 26:1–16)

The first step in the isolation of Jesus from everyone around Him began with the anticipation of His death. Jesus had known it all along. His enemies had talked about it for some time. He had told His uncomprehending disciples. Finally in Jerusalem at Passover time, what had been a potentiality began to turn into an inevitability.

For some time Jesus had been preparing His disciples for His impending death and resurrection (see Matt. 16:21; 17:22, 23; 20:18, 19). In His fourth death prediction, what did Jesus reveal to them? Why do you think He omitted reference to His resurrection at this time? (Matt. 26:1, 2)

. . . .

. . . .

What was the thinking of the religious authorities about dealing with Jesus who had so recently called them names and preached against them? (Matt. 26:3–5)

. . . .

. . . .

How did various ones react to the loving act of the woman who anointed Jesus' head with very costly perfume in Simon's house at Bethany?

◆ The disciples (Matt. 26:8, 9)

. . . .

. . . .

◆ Jesus (Matt. 26:10–13)

. . . .

. . . .

◆ Judas Iscariot (Matt. 26:14, 15)

. . . .

. . . .

How would Jesus have felt Himself separated from the following?

◆ The religious authorities

. . . .

. . . .

◆ His disciples

. . . .

. . . .

◆ Judas Iscariot

. . . .

. . . .

CONSIDER THIS

Read the *Word in Life™ Study Bible (WILSB)* feature "Judas Iscariot, the Betrayer" (Matt. 26:14–16). "No one knows what Judas' exact motives were for turning against Jesus. He remains a shadowy figure in the Gospel accounts."

The Old Testament reckoned thirty pieces of silver to be the fine levied on one who accidentally killed a slave (Ex. 21:32). Judas didn't betray Jesus for the money. What do you think may have motivated his villainy?

. . . .

. . . .

How did Judas' treachery alter the plans of the Sanhedrin? (Matt. 26:16, see v. 5)

. . . .

. . . .

◆ ALONE AS A PROPHET ◆

(Matthew 26:17–35)

The Passover meal had to be celebrated inside the city of Jerusalem, so pilgrims made arrangements with local residents. "Family" groupings traditionally consisted of a minimum of ten celebrants with the oldest or most authoritative presiding.[3] Jesus secured a Passover setting in a mysterious manner (Matt. 26:17–19) similar to the way the donkey for the Triumphal Entry was secured (21:1–6).

In the course of the meal that remembered redemption, Jesus told His disciples that one of them would betray Him (Matt. 26:20, 21). Why do you think each of the disciples asked if he was the betrayer? (Matt. 26:22)

. . . .

. . . .

Since all of the disciples wondered if they were the betrayer, how do you think the woe Jesus pronounced made them feel? (Matt. 26:23, 24)

. . . .

. . . .

It's not likely that the disciples understood much of what Jesus said as He instituted the Lord's Supper (Matt. 26:26–29). Their minds were occupied with the Passover and the disturbing talk of betrayal. When do you imagine they first began to realize the importance of His broken body and shed blood? What do you think it meant to them at that point?

. . . .

. . . .

What do you think Jesus wanted His disciples to understand when He told them they would all desert Him that night and that He would meet them again in Galilee? (Matt. 26:31, 32)

. . . .

. . . .

Why do you think Peter felt compelled to assert and reassert his allegiance to Jesus? (Matt. 26:33, 35)

. . . .

. . . .

How do you think Jesus wanted Peter to respond to His prediction that he would betray Him three times? (Matt. 26:34)

. . . .

. . . .

CONSIDER THIS

Read the *WILSB* feature "Would You Choose These for Leaders" (Matt. 26:35–74). "Jesus' treatment of the disciples shows that failure is not the unforgivable act. In fact, it seems to be the crucible out of which character is formed."

Circle the letter of the statement that best reflects how you would respond to a warning by a spiritual leader that he or she thought you were liable to fail under the pressures of a major crisis.

a. I would protest that I was prepared to deal with the crisis and determine to persevere and prove him or her wrong no matter what.

b. I would believe his or her assessment and withdraw from the coming crisis.

c. I would thank my leader for his or her insight and ask advice on how to approach the crisis.

d. I would figure that if he or she had no more confidence in me than that, I wouldn't try very hard in the crisis.

e. I would be crushed that I was thought vulnerable and would become depressed.

How does the Lord warn you about your weaknesses in order to prepare you for difficult situations ahead? How can you improve your response to His warnings?

. . . .

. . . .

Alone in Prayer
(Matthew 26:36–56)

As the drama of Jesus' arrest and trial began to unfold, all of the disciples of Jesus failed Him in one way or another. Perhaps each of them felt at some point that he was the betrayer Jesus had hinted at. In the Garden of Gethsemane, Jesus found Himself alone: first in prayer and finally in the presence of the armed multitude.

CONSIDER THIS

Read the *WILSB* feature "Praying in a Workplace" (Matt. 26:36). "The area around Jerusalem was rich with olive groves, and many people were employed at the commercial oil presses, or *gethsemanes,* to produce the city's only export product."

What did Jesus want from the three disciples He took with Him into the garden? (Matt. 26:36–38)

. . . .

. . . .

When Jesus prayed in the Garden of Gethsemane, what do you think His deepest desires were? (Matt. 26:39)

. . . .

. . . .

How did His prayer change as Jesus kept praying? (Matt. 26:39, 42)

. . . .

. . . .

In the light of what Jesus had said earlier, how do you think Peter and the sons of Zebedee (James and John) must have felt after they could not stay awake to support Him in prayer? (Matt. 26:40, 41, 43–46)

. . . .

. . . .

The religious authorities wanted to avoid a public arrest that would arouse sympathy for Jesus (Matt. 26:5). They were happy to make a quick night-time raid in an isolated place outside the city walls. The large force could handle any resistance from Jesus' entourage (v. 47). Judas' mock devotion was unconscionable (vv. 48, 49), but Jesus' question gave him a bizarre last chance to repent (v. 50).

Jesus had predicted His disciples would desert Him (Matt. 26:31). Why did He interfere with the disciple who drew his sword to prevent His arrest? (Matt. 26:51–54)

. . . .

. . . .

Why do you think Jesus' disciples deserted Him and fled when He said His arrest was in keeping with the Scriptures? (Matt. 26:55, 56)

. . . .

. . . .

When do you find it hardest to pray that God's will be done?

. . . .

. . . .

When do you find it hardest to refrain from lashing out at the opponents of the Lord?

. . . .

. . . .

Alone on Trial

(Matthew 26:57–68)

Jewish legal precedent forbade a nighttime trial, a trial outside the official chambers of the council, a capital verdict on the same day the charges were read, trial of a defendant without legal representation, and blasphemy charges unless the name of God was spoken. The authorities felt they had to ignore the niceties of the law in order to deal with Jesus rapidly (Matt. 26:57).

Why do you think Peter felt he had to stay with Jesus? (Matt. 26:58)

. . . .

. . . .

CONSIDER THIS

Read the *WILSB* feature "No Right Answers" (Matt. 26:59–68). "Some situations cannot be salvaged. . . . Like Jesus, however, believers can take hope that even in those moments, God remains in control."

Why do you think Jesus chose to remain silent while the council tried to trick Him with false interpretations of His own words? (Matt. 26:59–63)

. . . .

. . . .

The high priest put Jesus under oath and ordered Him to state whether He was the Messiah (Matt. 26:63). What did Jesus, the defendant, have to say to the high priest, the judge? (Matt. 26:64)

. . . .

. . . .

Describe a situation you faced where there was no way to save the situation with words of explanation or reconciliation. What happened? What consequences followed?

. . . .

. . . .

How have you trusted the Lord to deal with the aftermath of that situation?

. . . .

. . . .

How did the council decide that Jesus was worthy of death? (Matt. 26:65, 66)

. . . .

. . . .

◆ ALONE BY DENIAL ◆

(Matthew 26:69—27:10)

The dreadful isolation of Jesus through His arrest and trial had profound effects on Peter and Judas. Peter tried to be brave and carry out his boast to stay true to Jesus even if everyone else deserted Him. Judas began to realize the enormity of what he had done by betraying Jesus. Neither was prepared to deal with his situation.

Peter may have been caught off guard when it was just a servant girl who challenged him (Matt. 26:69). He couldn't knock her down or run her through. But she made her charge in front of others (v. 70). Peter caved in and denied Jesus. Why are little sneaky temptations sometimes more deadly than big obvious ones?

. . . .

. . . .

Once Peter had denied knowing Jesus, he couldn't change his story. He moved around to avoid further detection, but word seems to have circulated within the group in the courtyard that a disciple was among them (Matt. 26:71, 73). Peter used a stronger denial each time he was challenged about Jesus (vv. 72, 74). When are some times that you didn't want it known that you were a Christian?

. . . .

. . . .

Once the rooster crowed, Peter felt deep shame and went away to weep over his denial of Jesus (Matt. 27:75). When have you felt shame because of the way you concealed your faith in Christ? How did you express that shame?

. . . .

. . . .

How do you suppose Peter felt alienated by his denial from God, from the other disciples, and from himself?

. . . .

. . . .

The council composed of the chief priests and elders took Jesus to Pilate, the Roman governor, the next morning to get him to ratify their death sentence (Matt. 27:1, 2). By this time, Judas Iscariot had second thoughts about what he had done (v. 3). How did Judas deal with his regrets? (Matt. 27:3, 4, 5)

. . . .

. . . .

1. Aleksandr I. Solzhenitsyn, *The Gulag Archipelago*, 1918–1956, trans. by Thomas P. Whitney (New York: Harper & Row, Publishers, 1973), 7.

2. *Ibid.*, 9.

3. Craig S. Keener, 120.

LESSON 13

The Vanquishing King

Matthew 27:11—28:20

Aleksandr Solzhenitsyn surveyed the vast gulag of Soviet-era detention and torture and reflected on why a few defendants rose above the barbarism of their prosecutors to become beacons of heroism and hope to the few who managed to hear of them. As a prisoner he wondered how some prisoners, weakened and sensitive to pain, endured torture and abuse without caving in. He wondered how some men and women steeled themselves against thoughts and fears about the people they loved whom they left behind.

He concluded that anyone could be stronger than the interrogator and the whole Gulag. Solzhenitsyn realized that he had to reckon that his life was over. He would never return to freedom. That day, or the next, or next year he would die, and sooner would be better than later. He had no property. His loved ones were dead to him, and he to them. His body was useless to him and it deserved contempt. Only his spirit mattered and it had to be protected at all costs.

"Confronted by such a prioner," Solzhenitsyn asserted, "the interrogation will tremble.

"Only the man who has renounced everything can win the victory."[1]

Solzhenitsyn learned during eleven years in the gulag how to face torture and death. Jesus faced torture and death even more heroically because He knew He was doing it for the benefit of all who would believe in Him. He knew the Cross wasn't the end. He would rise again in victory over sin and death. The empty tomb vindicated the revolutionary gospel of Jesus the tender King.

The King Condemned

(Matthew 27:11–26)

Nobody liked Pontius Pilate. But that was all right because he didn't like them either. Probably the only reason he attempted to free Jesus was to spite the Jewish authorities who manipulated him. Jesus steeled Himself for the ordeal ahead and virtually ignored the pathetic powerbrokers who thought their words and actions so important.

Roman trials depended heavily on the initial statement of the accused in response to the charges. What do you think Pilate must have felt when Jesus wouldn't defend Himself? (Matt. 27:11–14)

. . . .

. . . .

The crowd gathered at the governor's residence probably was there to influence the annual Passover amnesty (Matt. 27:15). What did each of the following try to achieve through the amnesty choice of Jesus or Barabbas? (Matt. 27:15–21)

◆ Pilate

. . . .

. . . .

◆ Pilate's wife

. . . .

. . . .

◆ The chief priests and elders

. . . .

. . . .

◆ The crowd

. . . .

. . . .

The religious leaders apparently succeeded in using their authority to convince the mob that Jesus was a blasphemer and in appealing to the crowd's nationalism to choose the rebel Barabbas over Him.

Often when the tug-of-war of temptation to sin goes on in our heart and mind, we are as indifferent to the presence of Jesus as Pilate and the religious leaders were during their maneuvering on that Friday morning long ago. Circle the letter of the following statement that best describes how you can stop ignoring the Lord at those moments.

a. Remember that Satan wants to destroy me as much as he wanted to destroy Jesus.

b. Pray for strength and courage to face temptation in the way Jesus faced the cross.

c. Contemplate how the Lord resisted temptation when He encountered the devil.

d. Imagine Jesus anticipating crucifixion for the sin I'm considering.

e. Use Jesus' refusal to be drawn into the debate between Pilate and the religious leaders as a model for staying away from the pushes and pulls of temptation.

◆ THE KING EXECUTED ◆

(Matthew 27:27–56)

Jesus' crucifixion began with nearly universal scorn directed at Him. Jesus endured it without complaint until He sensed that His Father also had turned from Him. Then His anguish overwhelmed Him. But when He died, everyone knew something unusual and unnatural had occurred.

How did the Roman soldiers mock Jesus after scourging Him? (Matt. 27:27–31)

. . . .

. . . .

FOR YOUR INFO

"Crucifixion was the most shameful and painful form of execution known in antiquity. Stripped naked—especially shameful for Palestinian Jews—the condemned would be hanged in the sight of the crowds, regarded as a criminal, unable to restrain the excretion of wastes in public and subjected to excruciating torture. Sometimes the victim would be tied to the cross with ropes; in other cases, as with Jesus, he would be nailed to the cross. His hands would not be free to swat away insects attracted to his bloody back or other wounds. The victim's own weight would pull his body into a position that eventually prohibited breathing. A footstand on the cross allowed him some support, but sooner or later his strength would give out, and (usually after several days) he would die from suffocation."[2]

FOR YOUR INFO

Read the *Word in Life™ Study Bible (WILSB)* feature "The Little People at Jesus' Death" (Matt. 27:32). "Have you ever noticed that Jesus tended to surround Himself . . . by relatively average people of little social standing or influence?"

Why do you think Simon of Cyrene (Matt. 27:32) and the Galilean women (vv. 55, 56) receive recognition for their small roles in the crucifixion story?

. . . .

. . . .

Circle the number on the following scale that indicates how you would rate the social standing and influence of you and your circle of immediate friends.

1	2	3	4	5	6	7	8	9	10
UNDER-DOGS			MIXED BREEDS			FAVORITE PETS			TOP DOGS

How did each of these contribute to the suffering of Jesus as He hung on the cross?

◆ The Roman execution squad (Matt. 27:33–37)

. . . .

. . . .

◆ Passersby (Matt. 27:39, 40)

. . . .

. . . .

◆ The chief priests, scribes, and elders (Matt. 27:41– 43)

. . . .

. . . .

◆ The two thieves (Matt. 27:38, 44)

. . . .

. . . .

God darkened the sun from noon (sixth hour) until 3:00 P.M. (ninth hour) while His Son hung on the cross. Near the end of that time, what finally caused Jesus such agony that He could not bear it quietly? (Matt. 27:46)

. . . .

. . . .

How did the spectators interpret Jesus' outcry? (Matt. 27:47–49)

. . . .

. . . .

What supernatural signs accompanied the death of Jesus, the Son of God? (Matt. 27:51–53)

. . . .

. . . .

What did the execution-hardened centurion conclude on the basis of Jesus' death and its accompanying signs? (Matt. 27:54)

. . . .

. . . .

Circle the letter of the following statement that best represents your reaction to the story of the crucifixion.

a. The story grips my imagination and moves me with its terror and emotion.

b. I don't understand what motivates the characters of the crucifixion story to act as they do.

c. I think Jesus should have come down from the cross and blasted those who crucified and those who mocked Him.

d. I'm moved by my own sense of sinfulness and guilt as a cause of the death of Jesus.

e. It's so familiar that I have trouble sensing the horror and shame of the crucifixion.

The King Buried

(Matthew 27:57–66)

The prophet Isaiah had predicted that the Suffering Servant of the Lord would be associated with both the wicked and the rich in His death and burial (see Is. 53:9). While Jesus was crucified with two thieves, He was buried in the unused family tomb of a wealthy man.

FOR YOUR INFO

Read the *WILSB* feature "Wealthy People in the New Testament" (Matt. 27:57). "God calls believers to be compassionate, merciful, and just to all. Does your checkbook reflect such values?"

What was Joseph of Arimathea able to do as a wealthy disciple of Jesus that no one else could? (Matt. 27:57–60)

. . . .

. . . .

What risks did Joseph take as a prominent citizen by declaring His allegiance to Jesus after the religious authorities had condemned Him for blasphemy? (Matt. 27:57)

. . . .

. . . .

How does your pattern of giving and spending reflect a commitment to compassion, mercy, and justice?

. . . .

. . . .

What would you like to have the ability to do someday in the future with your wealth as an expression of your faith in Christ? What do you need to do to get to that point?

. . . .

. . . .

FOR YOUR INFO

"In the first century, the body would normally be left to rot in the tomb's antechamber for the first year; at the end of the year, the bones would be gathered into a box, which would slide into a slot in the wall. . . . The stone rolled in front of the tomb was a carved, disk-shaped stone probably about three feet in diameter, rolled into place in a groove and moved back from the entrance only with great effort."[3]

How were wealthy Joseph and the two poor Marys from Galilee alike in their devotion to Jesus? (Matt. 27:57–61)

. . . .

. . . .

The Day of Preparation (Matt. 27:62) was Friday. The next day was the Sabbath. What had troubled the chief priests (Sadducees) and Pharisees so much that they went to Pilate on a Sabbath? (Matt. 27:62–64)

. . . .

. . . .

It appears that Pilate told the chief priests and Pharisees to use their own guards, the temple police, to guard the tomb (Matt. 27:65).[4] How did they protect against the disciples stealing the body of Jesus? (Matt. 27:66)

. . . .

. . . .

In what ways do you observe people today trying to seal Jesus away lest He exert some kind of influence over them?

. . . .

. . . .

◆ THE KING RESURRECTED ◆

(Matthew 28:1–15)

It had never occurred to the chief priests and Pharisees that posting a guard at the tomb of Jesus would serve as evidence of the resurrection when He disappeared from the closely-watched tomb. They had claimed they would believe in Jesus if He defeated the cross and death (Matt. 27:42). However, when He did defeat death, they cooked up a lie to conceal the fact (28:12, 13).

How did the Lord reveal to the women that the tomb was empty and explain the significance of that emptiness? (Matt. 28:1–6)

. . . .

. . . .

What message did the angel give the women to relay to Jesus' disciples? (Matt. 28:7)

. . . .

. . . .

What emotional impact did the earthquake and angelic appearance have?

◆ On the guards (Matt. 28:4)

. . . .

. . . .

◆ On the women (Matt. 28:5, 8)

. . . .

. . . .

Why do you think Jesus appeared to the women who went to His tomb and reinforced the task the angels had given them? (Matt. 28:9, 10)

. . . .

. . . .

How did the chief priests exercise "damage control" when they found out that Jesus' tomb was empty in spite of their security efforts? (Matt. 28:11–14)

What was the result of their scheme? (Matt. 28:15)

What do you think motivates people today to explain away the biblical evidence for the resurrection of Jesus?

CONSIDER THIS

Read the *WILSB* feature "MYTH: There Is No Evidence That Jesus Rose from the Dead" (Matt. 28:1–10). "The question of whether Jesus actually rose from the dead is crucial. At least four lines of evidence indicate that He did."

1. What evidence supports the contention that Jesus certainly was dead?

2. What can be inferred from the fact that friends and enemies agreed Jesus' tomb certainly was empty?

3. What is the importance of Jesus' multiple post-resurrection appearances to individuals and groups of witnesses?

4. Of what value is the testimony of the changed lives of the disciples and Christians since to the truth of the resurrection?

5. Of what spiritual importance is the resurrection of Jesus to you personally?

. . . .

. . . .

◆ THE KING PROCLAIMED ◆

(Matthew 28:16–20)

Matthew stressed that Jesus the tender King began His ministry as a light dawning in the darkness of "Galilee of the Gentiles" (Matt. 4:15, 16). After His resurrection Jesus insisted on meeting His disciples again in this Jewish territory which had a strong Gentile presence. There He told His followers what the revolutionary future of the kingdom of heaven would involve.

It may be that the appearance of Jesus recorded in Matthew 28:16-20 was to more than 500 believers under the leadership of the eleven apostles (see 1 Cor. 15:6).[5] What was the response when they all saw the risen Lord? (Matt. 28:16, 17)

. . . .

. . . .

CONSIDER THIS

Read the *WILSB* feature "To All the Nations" (Matt. 28:19). "Today the bulk of new disciples are non-white and non-Western. Not surprisingly, they bring very different cultural perspectives into the church."

Describe the Great Commission of Jesus to His disciples according to these two categories.

◆ Its main tasks (Matt. 28:19)

. . . .

. . . .

◆ Its main methods (Matt. 28:19b, 20)

. . . .

. . . .

What were the great cultural biases the early disciples had to overcome to carry out the Great Commission?

. . . .

. . . .

What are some of the cultural biases we have to overcome to carry out the Great Commission as we face the twenty-first century?

. . . .

. . . .

Before your life is through, what would you consider the greatest adventure you could have in contributing to the spread of the gospel around the world? How could you prepare yourself to have this adventure?

. . . .

. . . .

1. Aleksandr I. Solzhenitsyn, 130.
2. Craig S. Keener, 126.
3. *Ibid.*, 129.
4. D. A. Carson, 586.
5. *Ibid.*, 589.

LEADER'S GUIDE

Small group studies succeed when all of the group members participate in discussion. As the leader you must be well-prepared, but your task is to stimulate the other group members to discover and apply the truths of the Bible passage under discussion. Discussion questions are your primary tool for guiding Bible exploration.

Good discussion questions are open-ended. Rather than asking for short, factual answers, they invite thinking about the text; looking beyond facts for spiritual principles, they explore the implication of the biblical truth for daily life. On the other hand, questions that can be answered "yes" or "no" effectively stifle discussion.

Discussion questions fall into three general categories.

Content questions invite exploration of the biblical text. Many of the questions in the *Bible Discovery Guide* are content questions. You may use some of the *Bible Discovery Guide* questions in your group discussions, but you will want to use other content questions to summarize what they learned in the *Bible Discovery Guide*.

Implication questions stimulate discussion of possible ways a biblical passage might be applied to life.

Application questions ask group members to formulate specific plans of action that implement biblical concepts in their lives.

Most discussion questions are content questions. Fewer are implication questions. Fewer still are application questions, but these may require the most time to answer satisfactorily.

The Leader's Guide provides additional content questions to summarize biblical material. Implication and application questions are provided for use or as models for your own questions. Each session plan contains many more questions than you can use in a typical hour-long Bible study. Be selective and creative.

Manage your session time carefully. Don't spend too much time on content questions so that your group fails to get to the implication and application phases. Don't allow a talkative group member to dominate discussion. When he or she takes a breath, thank him or her and ask for comments from others. Be careful not to be the dominant talker yourself.

If your group will be filling out the *Bible Discovery Guide* as part of your session, you must decide how much time you can devote to that activity. No one can complete a lesson in twenty minutes, so you may want to assign different parts of the study to different group members, and then each can make a contribution from his or her *Bible Discovery Guide* portions. In that way, each group member will bring a piece of the puzzle to the discussion and together the group assembles the whole picture.

LESSON 1
NO ORDINARY BEGINNING, NO ORDINARY KING
Matthew 1:1—2:23

SESSION AIMS

- ◆ To overview the scope and plan of Matthew's Gospel.
- ◆ To discover the extraordinary character of Jesus revealed in His genealogy and infancy stories.
- ◆ To explore how having "God with us" makes our ordinary lives extraordinary.

Read through the questions in this *Bible Discovery Guide* and select those that you want your group to discuss. Supplement those questions with any of the ones provided below. Arrange the questions in the order that seems best for your group. Be sure to familiarize yourself with the feature articles in this portion of the *Word in Life™ Study Bible.* These helps can greatly enrich your group's insights into God's Word.

WARMING UP

1. What is the most unusual birth story in your family?
2. When you were young, what child in your neighborhood seemed to have the most unusual life? What was different about it?

DIGGING IN

1. Why are biblical genealogies so uninteresting to modern readers?
2. Why do you suppose the original readers of the Bible valued these genealogies?
3. Why do you think Matthew included both spiritual giants and notable sinners in the genealogy of Jesus?
4. In your opinion, what did Matthew accomplish by means of his many Old Testament quotations?

5. What important roles did Joseph play in the birth and childhood of Jesus even though he wasn't His father?

6. Why do you suppose God directed Gentile wise men to be the ones who lavishly received Jesus as the new King of the Jews?

7. What did Herod's murderous hatred of Jesus foreshadow concerning His entire life?

8. Why do you think God chose to send His Son into a life marked by sorrow and poverty?

LOOKING FURTHER

1. How can you experience "God with us" through Jesus on an every-day basis?

2. How can your worship of the Lord become more sacrificial and lavish like that of the wise men?

3. How has the Lord protected you from dangers in the past? How does that affect your confidence for the present and the future?

4. What kind of person would you expect to grow and mature through the background and events of Matthew 1 and 2?

MAKING PLANS

1. Since you have come to faith in Jesus, what extraordinary things has God done in your life through "God with us"?

2. What do you know about God that you could only have learned through contact with Jesus ("God with us")?

Lesson 2
No Ordinary Teacher Certification
Matthew 3:1—5:16

SESSION AIMS

◆ To examine the credentials of Jesus to proclaim the good news of the kingdom of heaven.

◆ To discover the basis of His authority expressed in these stories.

◆ To evaluate the attitudes of my life by means of Jesus' Beatitudes.

Read through the questions in this *Bible Discovery Guide* and select those that you want your group to discuss. Supplement those questions with any of the ones provided below. Arrange the questions in the order that seems best for your group. Be sure to familiarize yourself with the feature articles in this portion of the *Word in Life™ Study Bible.* These helps can greatly enrich your group's insights into God's Word.

WARMING UP

1. Who was the best teacher you had in elementary school? What made that teacher outstanding to you?

2. Who is the best person you've ever known at quoting the Bible? When did you first notice this skill?

DIGGING IN

1. How did the ministry of John the Baptist prepare the way for Jesus?

2. What do you think Jesus' baptism by John meant?

3. What did the temptation of Jesus by the devil reveal about Jesus' character and approach to life?

4. What did the temptation of Jesus reveal about the character and goals of the devil?

5. What would you have predicted about the future success of Jesus' ministry from the early responses of the multitudes?

6. What seems to you to be the primary message of the Beatitudes of Jesus?

7. How do the gentle Beatitudes prepare believers in Christ to have mighty influence as salt or as the light of the world?

8. What do the baptism, the temptation, and the teaching of Jesus each show about His readiness to proclaim the kingdom of heaven?

LOOKING FURTHER

1. What have you learned about God and yourself through the process of repenting of your sins?

2. What does the example of Jesus teach you about how to resist the devil and his temptations to sin?

3. Which Beatitude do you need to work at most to align your life with the teaching of Jesus? Why this one?

4. In what parts of your Christian life does your light shine most brightly? In which parts is it dimmest?

MAKING PLANS

1. Either privately or openly identify a sinful practice or attitude that you plan to resist by means of Scripture and reliance on God's power.

2. In the margin of your Bible, write a day of the week next to each of the Beatitudes (Matt. 5:3–10). Concentrate on expressing one attitude or behavior each day this coming week. Plan to report about your experience next session.

Lesson 3
Getting to the Spirit of the Law
Matthew 5:17—6:18

SESSION AIMS

◆ To examine how the teaching of Jesus captured the spirit of the Law.

◆ To explore how goodness can overcome evil in daily life.

◆ To discover how to pray for the kingdom of heaven and for ourselves.

Read through the questions in this *Bible Discovery Guide* and select those that you want your group to discuss. Supplement those questions with any of the ones provided below. Arrange the questions in the order that seems best for your group. Be sure to familiarize yourself with the feature articles in this portion of the *Word in Life™ Study Bible.* These helps can greatly enrich your group's insights into God's Word.

WARMING UP

1. What's your favorite Old Testament story? How does it relate to the ideas of the New Testament?

2. When you first learned the Lord's Prayer, what did it mean to you? Which of its petitions stands out to you now as the most thought-provoking?

DIGGING IN

1. In what sense is anger as morally objectionable as murder?

2. In what sense is lust as morally objectionable as adultery?

3. How is a trustworthy "yes" and "no" morally superior to an elaborate system of oaths?

4. What is the moral strength inherent in refusing to fight with a bully?

5. What makes loving one's enemies one of the most revolutionary ideas the tender Messiah taught?

6. Why do we always have to resist the temptation to behave righteously in order to be approved by observers?

LOOKING FURTHER

1. What emotion—anger, lust, or some other—do you need to conquer in order to obey the spirit of the law?

2. What could you do to improve the integrity of your "yes" and your "no"?
3. In what area(s) of your life do you think the Lord wants you to try and overcome evil with good right now? Why?

4. How would following the example of the Lord's Prayer improve your daily private praying?

MAKING PLANS

1. In the area of life you mentioned in an earlier question, what specific steps should you take to try to overcome evil with good?

2. What should you be praying for regularly to advance the kingdom of heaven locally and around the world?

3. According to the Lord's Prayer, how should you be praying for yourself?

Lesson 4
A Revolution In Values
Matthew 6:19—7:29

SESSION AIMS

◆ To clarify the value system taught by Jesus in the Sermon on the Mount.

◆ To identify deficiencies in my personal value system.

◆ To determine how to align my values with those of Jesus.

Read through the questions in this *Bible Discovery Guide* and select those that you want your group to discuss. Supplement those questions with any of the ones provided below. Arrange the questions in the order that seems best for your group. Be sure to familiarize yourself with the feature articles in this portion of the *Word in Life™ Study Bible.* These helps can greatly enrich your group's insights into God's Word.

WARMING UP

1. Tell of an instance, as a child or an adult, when you really thought you wanted something, but when you got it the item wasn't as great as you had expected.

2. Outside of spiritual treasures, what is your most valued possession? What makes it precious to you?

DIGGING IN

1. What's the relationship between who our master is and what we concern ourselves about?

2. Although people aren't birds or wildflowers, what lessons can we learn from them about God's care for us?

3. What did Jesus say about judging others—don't do it, be kind, be fair, or what?

4. Matthew 7:13–27 presents a series of paired opposites. What would you say all of these pairs have in common?

LOOKING FURTHER

1. Why do you suppose we worry so readily about our physical wellbeing and ignore so easily our spiritual wellbeing?

2. What do you think God has promised to do for you if you seek first His kingdom and His righteousness?

3. How does the Golden Rule help in deciding when to make a judgment and when to refrain?

4. Why do you suppose we are more inclined to point out others' specks when we have planks in our own eyes?

5. When you pray, how do you think God reacts emotionally to what you say to Him?

6. How do the ideas about the wide and narrow gates, the good and bad trees, and the houses built on sand and rock motivate you to tell others about Jesus?

MAKING PLANS

1. How can you increase your peace of mind without ignoring your financial and personal responsibilities?

2. How should you adjust your pattern of judging others on the basis of Jesus' teaching?

Lesson 5
No Ordinary Power
Matthew 8:1—10:42

SESSION AIMS

- To survey this record of Jesus' miracles and personal authority.
- To explore what the miracles revealed about Jesus and the world around Him.
- To consider how the power of Jesus affects the lives of Christians today.

Read through the questions in this *Bible Discovery Guide* and select those that you want your group to discuss. Supplement those questions with any of the ones provided below. Arrange the questions in the order that seems best for your group. Be sure to familiarize yourself with the feature articles in this portion of the *Word in Life™ Study Bible.* These helps can greatly enrich your group's insights into God's Word.

WARMING UP

1. What's the most powerful natural phenomenon you've ever witnessed? How did it make you feel?
2. Are you attracted to or repelled by powerful people? Why?

DIGGING IN

1. What different kinds of people did Jesus help in Matthew 8? What does this diversity suggest about the kingdom of God?
2. Why do you suppose there's a paragraph about Jesus' homelessness (Matt. 8:18–22) in the middle of a chapter about His great power?
3. How did Jesus perceive the faith of various people He helped in Matthew 9?
4. Matthew wrote that Jesus felt compassion for the multitudes (9:36). How many reasons can you think of for His compassion?

5. Why do you think Jesus sent out His disciples to preach and heal in His name when they still understood so little about Him and the kingdom?

6. Why do you think disciples of Jesus have to expect so much resistance and persecution?

LOOKING FURTHER

1. How can you expect the physical authority of Jesus to affect your life?

2. How can you expect the spiritual authority of Jesus to affect your life?

3. What kinds of authority do you expect the Lord to delegate to you as you serve Him? Why?

4. What do you think it means to be a sheep among wolves while being wise as serpents and harmless as doves (Matt. 10:16)?

MAKING PLANS

1. Name a physical and a spiritual way you would like to see the power of Jesus expressed in your life right now.

2. What teaching on prayer in Matthew should encourage you to pray and ask others to pray for the power of Christ in your life?

3. How would you like the power of Christ to aid you in your witness for Him?

LESSON 6
DRAWING A LINE IN THE SAND
Matthew 11:1—13:52

SESSION AIMS

◆ To trace the rise of opposition to the ministry of Jesus.

◆ To evaluate the charges made by opponents to discredit Jesus.

◆ To identify the everyday conflicts between good and evil in my spheres of influence.

Read through the questions in this *Bible Discovery Guide* and select those that you want your group to discuss. Supplement those questions with any of the ones provided below. Arrange the questions in the order that seems best for your group. Be sure to familiarize yourself with the feature articles in this portion of the *Word in Life*™ *Study Bible.* These helps can greatly enrich your group's insights into God's Word.

WARMING UP

1. Who's the best storyteller among your family or friends? What makes his or her stories so good?

2. What's the worst untrue thing anyone ever said about you? How did you feel at the time?

DIGGING IN

1. Matthew 12:18–21 quotes one of the Suffering Servant passages from Isaiah (42:1–4). What does this long quote have to say about the character of Jesus?

2. Why did the Pharisees feel they needed to attribute Jesus' power over demons to the devil himself? How would they have tried to explain the logic of their explanation?

3. How did the scribes and Pharisees react when they actually saw "the sign of Jonah the prophet"?

4. Do you think the parable of the four soils applies to people's first encounter with the gospel or every contact with the Word of God? Why?

5. How do you figure that parables conceal the truth (Matt. 13:15), and how do they reveal it (v. 35)?

6. How do you suppose the enemy sows tares among the wheat of the kingdom of heaven?

LOOKING FURTHER

1. What burdens do you need Jesus to bear with you so you can find rest for your soul?

2. What objections do people make to yoking themselves with Jesus, even though His yoke is comfortable and rewarding?

3. Have you ever worried about committing the unpardonable sin? If so, what had you done that concerned you so? Were you confusing the power of God and the power of Satan?

4. Do you find Jesus' parables confusing or clarifying? Why?

5. When others explain Jesus' parables to you, do their explanations help or make things worse? Why?

MAKING PLANS

1. Who in your life is the primary opponent of the Christian faith with whom you must deal? What seems to be his or her primary objection(s) to Christianity?

2. Would you say this person's main difficulty with Christianity arises from his or her wrong attitudes, wrong understanding of the Bible, or wrong spiritual commitment? Why would you say this?

3. When you respond to the Word of God, which kind of soil are you most of the time: hard, shallow, thorny, or good? Why do you say so?

LESSON 7
CHOOSING SIDES IN THE REVOLUTION
Matthew 13:53—16:28

SESSION AIMS

◆ To explore the intensifying attitudes for and against the ministry of Jesus.

◆ To examine the concern of Jesus for needy people in the face of intensifying opposition.

◆ To consider the strength of my loyalty to Jesus when opposed by powerful social and political forces.

Read through the questions in this *Bible Discovery Guide* and select those that you want your group to discuss. Supplement those questions with any of the ones provided below. Arrange the questions in the order that seems best for your group. Be sure to familiarize yourself with the feature articles in this portion of the *Word in Life™ Study Bible*. These helps can greatly enrich your group's insights into God's Word.

WARMING UP

1. What's the worst difference of opinion you have ever been a part of? What happened because of this sharp disagreement?

2. Has anyone here ever witnessed a feud between two families? What started the feud in the first place? What kinds of offenses kept it going?

DIGGING IN

1. Why do you think the familiarity of residents of Nazareth with Jesus caused them to be offended by His authority?

2. How did Herod have more to lose by killing John the Baptist than Herodias did? Is her guilt more than his? Why?

3. What do you think Jesus expected His disciples to do when He told them to feed the multitude?

4. In Matthew 15:7 Jesus called the scribes and Pharisees hypocrites for the first time. How did they earn this denunciation?

5. Are you surprised that Jesus was reluctant to heal the Canaanite woman's daughter and made her talk Him into healing her? Why or why not?

6. Why would Matthew record both the feeding of the 5,000 and the feeding of the 4,000 when they're so similar?

7. What do you think it was about the teaching of the scribes and Pharisees that Jesus regarded as dangerous yeast permeating the Jewish mindset of the day?

8. How could Peter be so clear about who Jesus was and so foggy about what He had come to do?

LOOKING FURTHER

1. How do you react to the news that someone has been martyred for faith in Christ?

2. When have you felt that the Lord was asking you to do something you were not prepared to do? What happened?

3. Do you think Christian traditions stand in the way of the growth of the kingdom, or do you think our traditions are necessary for solid expansion? Why?

4. When you are under pressure, how can you still make time to care for the needy?

5. What attitudes of the popular culture must we keep from corrupting our devotion to Christ?

6. How can you keep from inadvertently opposing the purposes of the Lord as Peter did?

MAKING PLANS

1. What popular political and social trends seem to you to oppose attitudes and values Jesus promoted? Why do you think so?

2. What do you think is the most effective way to express your Christian conviction about these political and social trends?

LESSON 8
20–20 FAITH
Matthew 17:1—19:30

SESSION AIMS

◆ To discover why faith can "see" spiritual truth while unbelief is "blind."

◆ To explore characteristics of the "seeing" faith Jesus taught.

◆ To test whether my faith "sees" the things Jesus wants me to.

Read through the questions in this *Bible Discovery Guide* and select those that you want your group to discuss. Supplement those questions with any of the ones provided below. Arrange the questions in the order that seems best for your group. Be sure to familiarize yourself with the feature articles in this portion of the *Word in Life™ Study Bible.* These helps can greatly enrich your group's insights into God's Word.

WARMING UP

1. Tell about a time when you realized that your eyesight was definitely better or worse than that of most people.

2. How many people in the group had to have glasses as a child? How did you feel about it? How did your vision change when you got them?

DIGGING IN

1. Why do you think Jesus invested more time and attention with Peter, James, and John than the other disciples?

2. Jesus said the disciples could not heal the epileptic boy because of unbelief. In what way do you think their faith was weak?

3. What is it about childlike faith that makes the one who has it greatest in the kingdom of heaven?

4. How can you tell the difference between an intentionally exaggerated statement in the Bible and a literal statement of an extreme truth?

5. What do you suppose repeated forgiveness of one's Christian brother or sister has to do with the strength of one's faith?

6. Why do you think human "hardness of heart" prompted God to permit divorce under the Mosaic Law?

7. How do you figure that adultery severs the marriage bond that God intended to be permanent when other things don't?

8. For the rich young ruler, what was the relationship among faith, keeping the commandments, and giving away his wealth?

LOOKING FURTHER

1. What means does the Lord regularly use to remind you to listen to His Son? How well do you heed the reminders?

2. In what ways would you like your faith to be more childlike?

3. Why do you think we are to be absolutely ruthless with the sin in our own life but forgiving of the sins in the lives of others?

4. Why do you suppose the united action of two or three Christians carries so much weight with the Lord?

5. How can you forgive someone's repeated sins without condoning them?

6. How do good incomes, various kinds of insurance, and retirement programs affect the faith of Christians in developed nations?

7. Has your faith in Christ ever led you to sacrifice advancement or success for the cause of the kingdom? If so, how?

MAKING PLANS

1. Identify something the Lord has recently been trying to get you to "see" with the eyes of faith.

2. What do you need to do to sharpen your spiritual vision to "see" what the Lord is showing you?

3. Are childlikeness or forgiveness issues clarifying your faith vision? If so, what do you need to do about them?

Lesson 9
Who Said Faith Is Easy?
Matthew 20:1—21:46

SESSION AIMS

◆ To explore factors that impede the growth or exercise of faith.

◆ To discover what hindrances to faith really irritated Jesus.

◆ To consider how much influence power and wealth have on my faith in Christ.

Read through the questions in this *Bible Discovery Guide* and select those that you want your group to discuss. Supplement those questions with any of the ones provided below. Arrange the questions in the order that seems best for your group. Be sure to familiarize yourself with the feature articles in this portion of the *Word in Life™ Study Bible.* These helps can greatly enrich your group's insights into God's Word.

WARMING UP

1. Describe a trip on which it seemed you would never get where you were heading. What hindered your progress?

2. Who do you know who is skeptical of everything? Why does that person have trouble believing anything?

DIGGING IN

1. The parable of the wages (Matt. 20:1–16) is not about how much the laborers worked; it's about how the landowner paid. What was Jesus illustrating about God?

2. How can God's graciousness seem unjust to people who feel they have worked really hard for Him?

3. When Jesus told the sons of Zebedee about His baptism and a cup, what was He alluding to? Why didn't James and John know what He was talking about? Hadn't Jesus told them?

4. How did the physical blindness of the two men at Jericho compare to the spiritual blindness of Jesus' disciples?

5. What did the people who accompanied Jesus on His Triumphal Entry realize about Him and what did they not realize?

6. Why wouldn't the chief priests and elders answer Jesus' question about John the Baptist?

7. How was Jesus protected from the religious leaders by His widespread popularity among ordinary people?

LOOKING FURTHER

1. How will a sense that God owes you something hinder strong faith?

2. How will a desire for power and prestige hinder your faith?

3. How can a Christian find out where his or her spiritual blind spots are?

4. How does rejecting spiritual correction hinder the growth of your faith?

5. What will happen to your faith if you are in the habit of promising to obey God but not doing it?

MAKING PLANS

1. What person do you admire most? What qualities of that person earned your respect?

2. How would you evaluate that person spiritually? Is he or she a person of humble, servant faith?

3. What does your choice of hero suggest about the strength or weakness of power and wealth as influences on your faith in Christ?

Lesson 10
Unbelief: Playing With Fire
Matthew 22:1—23:39

SESSION AIMS

◆ To examine Jesus' description of the nature of unbelief.

◆ To consider what the greatest dangers of unbelief are.

◆ To look for ways my religious routines may provide hiding places for unbelief.

Read through the questions in this *Bible Discovery Guide* and select those that you want your group to discuss. Supplement those questions with any of the ones provided below. Arrange the questions in the order that seems best for your group. Be sure to familiarize yourself with the feature articles in this portion of the *Word in Life™ Study Bible.* These helps can greatly enrich your group's insights into God's Word.

WARMING UP

1. When you were a child, was there someone in your town or neighborhood that all the kids feared as some sort of monster? If so, why was this person regarded as an ogre?

2. When have you embarrassed yourself by refusing to believe something that turned out to be true? How did you feel, and how did other people react when you turned out to be wrong?

DIGGING IN

1. How had the chief priests and Pharisees behaved like the invited wedding guests who snubbed and angered their king?

2. How were many ordinary Jews like the back-up guest who offended his king by coming to the celebration in everyday clothes?

3. What do you think the Pharisees and Sadducees expected to accomplish if they had tripped up Jesus with their trick questions?

4. Why would it have been incredible to the religious leaders for David to call his descendant Lord?

5. Why did Jesus object to His disciples bearing titles of respect and authority? Do you think this is a strict prohibition? Why or why not?

6. The Pharisees were the best evangelists prior to the Christians. How did Jesus fault their zeal for making converts?

7. Why did the Pharisees think they were totally different from their ancestors who had killed the Old Testament prophets? How could Jesus say they were just like those murderous ancestors?

LOOKING FURTHER

1. What gracious offers by God can we ignore and by so doing offend and anger Him?

2. Generally speaking, what things do you think belong to Caesar and what things belong to God?

3. How do people adjust the truth of the Bible to make it fit the preferences of our day?

4. When have you found yourself saying, in effect, "Do as I say, not as I do"?

5. What do you think are the most dangerous forms of hypocrisy in the church today?

MAKING PLANS

1. As you studied Matthew 22 and 23, which expression of unbelief impressed you as the one you most need to avoid? Why do you feel susceptible to this one?

2. How can religious routines cover up inactive or weakening faith? What would you do if you thought this was happening to you?

3. Which aspects of your daily or weekly spiritual practices are a little mechanical right now? How can you put some life and spontaneity back into them?

LESSON 11
FAITH PENETRATES THE FUTURE
Matthew 24:1—25:46

SESSION AIMS

◆ To analyze Jesus' teachings about the future and the last days.

◆ To explore the attitudes believers are to have toward the last days.

◆ To rate my preparedness for the return of Jesus.

Read through the questions in this *Bible Discovery Guide* and select those that you want your group to discuss. Supplement those questions with any of the ones provided below. Arrange the questions in the order that seems best for your group. Be sure to familiarize yourself with the feature articles in this portion of the *Word in Life™ Study Bible.* These helps can greatly enrich your group's insights into God's Word.

WARMING UP

1. How many of you went through a time when you were so certain that Jesus would return soon that you never expected to reach your current age? How does that make you think about His return now?

2. When you were a child, how did you feel during the period between Thanksgiving and Christmas? What did you do to hurry the time along?

DIGGING IN

1. Why do you think Jesus considered the fall of Jerusalem in A.D. 70 a good preview of the tribulation before His second coming?

2. How will people be able to distinguish the second coming from the arrival of any false messiah?

3. In what sense will the Son of Man return "at an hour when you do not expect" (Matt. 24:44)? Is He trying to trick people?

4. Why is it unacceptable to God for one to be unwatchful and unprepared when Jesus returns?

5. What do you think the "joy of the Lord" is that the diligent managers were promised in the parable?

6. Who do you suppose Jesus meant by "My brethren" (Matt. 25:40) in the judgment of the sheep and goats?

7. Why do you think the punishment of the faithless characters in all of Jesus' end-time parables is so violently severe?

LOOING FURTHER

1. Why do you suppose so many people fall for false messiahs and predictions of the return of Christ in spite of Jesus' warnings against such things?

2. What are the responsibilities you need to perform faithfully as you watch for the Lord's return?

3. What spiritual disciplines do you maintain to stay prepared for the return of the Lord?

4. What is the stewardship God has given you to maintain diligently until the Lord returns?

5. How do you put your compassion for the needy into action as you wait for the return of the Lord?

MAKING PLANS

1. What would Jesus approve of in your life if He returned tomorrow?

2. What would you want to be different about your life if Jesus were returning tomorrow?

3. How can you keep yourself mindful of the imminence of His return?

LESSON 12
THE ABANDONED KING
Matthew 26:1—27:10

SESSION AIMS

◆ To compare the isolating effects on Jesus of hostile enemies and disloyal friends.

◆ To contemplate the combined effect on Jesus of all of the rejection He experienced.

◆ To trace the guilt and shame experienced by Jesus' disciples.

◆ To identify and confess my own acts of rejection and denial of the Lord Jesus.

Read through the questions in this *Bible Discovery Guide* and select those that you want your group to discuss. Supplement those questions with any of the ones provided below. Arrange the questions in the order that seems best for your group. Be sure to familiarize yourself with the feature articles in this portion of the *Word in Life™ Study Bible.* These helps can greatly enrich your group's insights into God's Word.

WARMING UP

1. What's the most isolated from all other people that you've ever been in your life? How did that experience make you feel?

2. When you were a child, who was the kid in the neighborhood who always tattled on everybody else? What did the other kids think about the tattler?

DIGGING IN

1. What was wrong with the disciples' complaint that the woman who anointed Jesus was wasteful?

2. Do you think Judas realized when he went to the Passover meal that Jesus knew he was betraying Him? Why or why not?

3. How do you suppose Jesus could keep His mind on instituting the Lord's Supper when He knew what was going to happen right afterwards?

4. What do you think it would have meant to Jesus if Peter, James, and John had watched and prayed with Him in the Garden of Gethsemane?

5. When Jesus said, "All who take the sword will perish by the sword," was He advocating some form of pacifism? Why or why not?

6. Matthew called those who testified before the council false witnesses. Do you think he meant they were deliberate liars or that they misunderstood everything they tried to remember? Why?

7. How do you think the council members felt when Jesus did not prophesy who was spitting on Him and slapping Him?

8. If all the disciples deserted Jesus in the Garden of Gethsemane, how was it that Peter followed the arresting party right into the courtyard of the high priest's home?

9. In light of all the humiliation Jesus experienced after His arrest, why do you suppose Judas decided He was innocent?

LOOKING FURTHER

1. When you don't understand what the Lord is doing in your life, do you wait for clarification or move ahead as best you can? Why?

2. When you desert or betray the Lord by making sinful choices, how do you think it affects Him personally?

3. Have you ever tried, like Peter, to be spiritually courageous when in fact you were very weak spiritually? What happened?

4. What was wrong with the way Judas responded to his remorse over betraying Jesus? Have you ever felt a similar remorse? How did you deal with it?

MAKING PLANS

1. What past or present actions make you feel guilty as though you have betrayed or denied the Lord?

2. Let's spend a few moments in silent prayer confessing and asking forgiveness for these acts of betrayal or denial. Then one member will pray aloud for the group.

3. How can you find God's strength to respond differently in the future?

LESSON 13
THE VANQUISHING KING
Matthew 27:11—28:20

SESSION AIMS

- ◆ To survey the abuse Jesus endured from various sources.
- ◆ To note the supernatural displays that validated Jesus' divinity.
- ◆ To contrast the futility of the authorities' precautions with the triumph of Jesus' resurrection.
- ◆ To explore how I ought to carry out the Great Commission of Jesus.

Read through the questions in this *Bible Discovery Guide* and select those that you want your group to discuss. Supplement those questions with any of the ones provided below. Arrange the questions in the order that seems best for your group. Be sure to familiarize yourself with the feature articles in this portion of the *Word in Life™ Study Bible.* These helps can greatly enrich your group's insights into God's Word.

WARMING UP

1. When was the last time you felt like cheering when the "good guys" snatched victory from the jaws of defeat?
2. What's the most thrilling missionary story you have ever heard?

DIGGING IN

1. Why was it a mistake for Pilate to try to reason with the mob demanding Jesus' crucifixion?
2. What was Pilate trying to do by washing his hands before the mob? Why was this legally and morally meaningless?
3. How does the treatment of Jesus by the soldiers reflect Roman anti-semitism?
4. How do you imagine that the mood of the onlookers at Jesus' crucifixion changed as time passed and Jesus didn't do anything to save Himself?

5. Explain the irony of the chief priests and Pharisees calling Jesus a deceiver and accusing Him of deception when they asked Pilate to guard Jesus' tomb.

6. Compare and contrast the reactions of the big, brave guards and the helpless women to the earthquake and the angel at the tomb.

7. Why do you think Jesus honored the women with His first post-resurrection appearance?

8. What attitudes and actions of the disciples throughout Matthew make them seem unlikely candidates to take the gospel to the whole world?

9. What resources did Jesus provide His disciples for the task of world evangelization?

LOOKING FURTHER

1. When is it best to refuse to get into arguments with critics of the Christian faith?

2. Under what kinds of circumstances is it morally best to accept suffering without protest or self-defense?

3. What is the difference between the personal risks prominent and obscure people take when they declare their allegiance to Christ?

4. How does the responsibility for carrying out the Great Commission apply to lay people as well as ministers and missionaries?

MAKING PLANS

1. How can you help skeptical unbelievers understand the strength of the historical evidence for the resurrection of Jesus?

2. What can you do to spread the gospel of Christ at home and around the world?

Resources for Study Leaders from Thomas Nelson Publishers

McDonald, William. *Believer's Bible Commentary: New Testament.* Excellent, easily grasped comments on all of the books of the New Testament.

Nelson's Complete Book of Bible Maps and Charts: Old and New Testaments. Excellent source of handouts and teaching visual aids.

Nelson's Illustrated Encyclopedia of Bible Facts. A comprehensive sourcebook on all the people, places, and customs of the Bible.

Nelson's New Illustrated Bible Dictionary. Descriptions (many illustrated) of people, places, things, and ideas of the Bible.

Nelson's Quick Reference Bible People and Places. A pocket-sized guide with thumbnail sketches of everyone and every place in the Bible.

NKJV Exhaustive Concordance. An essential reference work for locating words and passages.

Vine's Complete Expository Dictionary of Old and New Testament Words. Ready nontechnical access to insight into the Greek or Hebrew words behind the English translation.

Vos, Howard F. *Nelson's Quick Reference Introduction to the Bible.* A pocket-sized Bible handbook that captures the highlights of every book.

Wiersbe, Warren W. *With the Word.* A chapter-by-chapter Bible handbook with a warm devotional emphasis.

Wilkinson, Bruce and Boa, Kenneth. *Talk Thru the Bible.* Overview information about every book of the Bible. Excellent charts and maps.